GLENCOE

# Backpack Reader

COURSE **3** BOOK **2**

WITH A
*GRAPHIC NOVEL*
*IN EVERY UNIT!*

www.glencoe.com

Mc Graw Hill **Glencoe**

New York, New York    Columbus, Ohio    Chicago, Illinois    Peoria, Illinois    Woodland Hills, California

# Acknowledgments

Grateful acknowledgment is given authors, publishers, photographers, museums, and agents for permission to reprint the following copyrighted material. Every effort has been made to determine copyright owners. In case of any omissions, the Publisher will be pleased to make suitable acknowledgments in future editions.
*Acknowledgments continued on page R3.*

 **Glencoe**

The *McGraw-Hill* Companies

Send all inquiries to:
**Glencoe/McGraw-Hill**
8787 Orion Place
Columbus, OH 43240-4027
ISBN-13: 978-0-07-874337-5
ISBN-10: 0-07-874337-0

Printed in the United States of America.

2 3 4 5 6 7 8 9 110/055 10 09 08 07

# Table of Contents

# Table of Contents

## UNIT 8  What is the American Dream?

# How do you stay true to yourself?

How do you know who you are? Are you what you look like? Are you what you do? As you read the following selections, you'll discover a variety of ways in which to think about the question: **How do you stay true to yourself?**

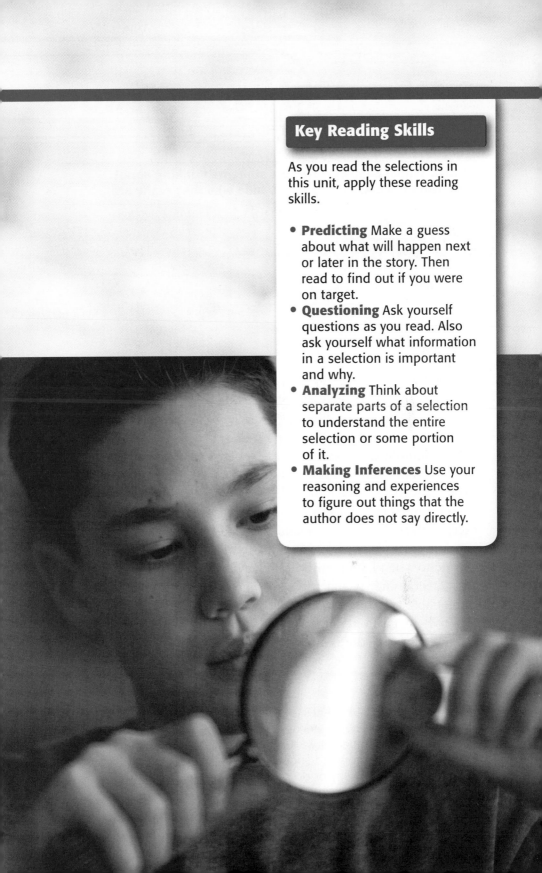

## Key Reading Skills

As you read the selections in this unit, apply these reading skills.

- **Predicting** Make a guess about what will happen next or later in the story. Then read to find out if you were on target.
- **Questioning** Ask yourself questions as you read. Also ask yourself what information in a selection is important and why.
- **Analyzing** Think about separate parts of a selection to understand the entire selection or some portion of it.
- **Making Inferences** Use your reasoning and experiences to figure out things that the author does not say directly.

# *from* **Bronx Masquerade**

## by Nikki Grimes

**A high school English class gets students thinking about removing the masks they use to hide who they really are.**

### Zorro

### by Raul Ramirez

**C**all me Zorro, all <u>swash</u> and buckle while the cameras roll, cape swinging in the breeze, teeth showing as expected. I <u>lunge</u> on <u>cue</u>, save the damsel in distress. I understand my role. I've studied all those <u>scripts</u> and comic books. I used to pose for close-ups, knew how to dutifully disappear when the script said: "Fade to black." Then I'd wait uncomfortably between the lines of my own story 'til someone with skin like milk yelled "Action!" But I'm done. I'm too old for comic heroes. It's time to lose the cape, step off the page, except I think I'll keep the mask. Why make it easy for you to choose whether I am Zorro or el bandito when I am neither? Your categories are too confusing. The fact is, you're more comfortable with myth than man. But I am here to help. First off, put down your camera. Second, give me your hand. ❶

> ❶ **Analyzing**
> What is the main idea, or message, of Raul's essay?

---

## Vo•cab•u•lary

**masquerade** (mas kuh RAYD) an event in which people wear costumes; a disguise or pretense
**swash** (swosh) swagger, or walk in a boastful way
**lunge** (lunj) to move forward suddenly
**cue** (kyoo) a signal to say or do something
**scripts** (skripts) the texts of a play or movie

# DIONDRA JORDAN

If only I was as bold as Raul. The other day, he left one of his paintings on Mr. Ward's desk where anybody could see it. Which was the point. He sometimes works at Mr. Ward's desk during lunch. The wet paintbrushes sticking up out of the jar are always a sign that he's been at it again. So of course, anybody who glances over in that direction will be tempted to stop by and look.

This particular painting was rough, but anyone could tell it was Raul. A self-portrait. He'll probably hang it in class. Back in September, Mr. Ward covered two of the classroom walls with black construction paper and then scattered paper frames up and down the walls, each one a different size and color. Now half the room looks sort of like an art gallery, which was the idea. We're supposed to use the paper frames for our work. Whether we put up poems or photographs or even paintings is up to us, so long as the work is ours and we can tie it in with our study of the Harlem Renaissance. I guess Raul's self-portrait fits, since we've been talking a lot about identity. He'll probably put it up next to his poem. You should have seen him hang that thing. You'd think he was handling a million-dollar <u>masterpiece</u> the way he took his time placing it just so. If you look close, you can see the smudges where he erased a word or two and rewrote it. Mr. Ward must be

---

## Vo•cab•u•lary

**masterpiece** (MAS tur pees) an outstanding work; a person's best achievement

3

in shock. He can never get Raul to rewrite a lick of homework or anything else. And don't even talk to him about checking his spelling! He'll launch into a <u>tirade</u> on you in a minute. "What?" he'll snap. "You think Puerto Ricans can't spell?" Forget it. Anyway, I dare you to find one misspelled word in that poem of his! Maybe it's a visual thing. Maybe he wants his poem to look as good as his self-portrait. And it is good.

I've never tried doing a self-portrait, but why not? I could maybe do one in charcoal. I've been drawing since I can't remember when. Not that anyone here knows that, except Tanisha, and she found out by accident when she came to my house to study once and saw a couple of drawings hanging in my room. Mom loves my watercolors and she hung one in the living room, but it isn't signed. Nobody ever mentions it, especially not my father. He's not too wild about my art. Mostly, he's disappointed, first off that I wasn't born a boy, and second that I won't play ball like one. I'm six feet tall, almost as tall as he, and he figures the height is wasted on me since I don't share his dreams of me going to the WNBA. I keep telling him not to hold his breath.

I hate always being the tallest girl in school. Everybody expects me to play basketball, so they pick me for their team, throw me the ball, and wait for me to shoot. Big mistake. I fumble it every time. Then they have the nerve to get mad at me, like I did it on purpose! But basketball is not my game. I have no game. I'm an artist, like Raul. The difference is, I don't tell anybody. I refuse to give them new reasons to laugh at me. The Jolly Green Giant jokes are bad enough.

Yeah, it's definitely time to try a self-portrait. I think I'll paint myself in front of an easel. With a basketball jersey sticking up out of the trash. ❷ Then I could hang it in Mr. Ward's class. See if anybody notices.

> ❷ **Making Inferences**
> How will Diondra's self-portrait reflect her true self?

### Vo·cab·u·lary

**tirade** (TY rayd) a long and angry speech

## Devon Hope

**J**ump shot. What kind of name is that? Not mine, but try telling that to the brothers at school. That's all they ever call me.

You'd think it was written somewhere. Tall guys must be jocks. No. Make that tall people, 'cause Diondra's got the same problem. Everybody expects her to shoot hoops. The difference is, she's got no talent in that direction. Ask me, she's got no business playing b-ball. That's my game.

I've got good height and good hands, and that's a fact. But what about the rest of me? Forget who I really am, who I really want to be. The law is be cool, be tough, play ball, and use books for weight training—not reading. Otherwise, everybody gives you grief. Don't ask me why I care, especially when the grief is coming from a punk like Wesley. Judging from the company he keeps, he's a gangsta in sheep's clothing. I don't even know why he and Tyrone even bother coming to school. It's clear they don't take it seriously, although maybe they're starting to. That's according to Sterling, who believes in praying for everybody and giving them the benefit of the doubt. I love the preacher-man, but I think he may be giving these brothers too much credit. Anyway, when I hang around after school and any of the guys ask me: "Yo, Devon, where you going?" I tell them I'm heading for the gym to meet Coach and work on my layup. Then once they're out the door, I cut upstairs to the library to sneak a read.

## from **Bronx Masquerade**

It's not much better at home. My older brother's always after me to hit the streets with him, calls me a girly man for loving books and jazz.

Don't get me wrong. B-ball is all right. Girls like you, for one thing. But it's not *you* they like. It's Mr. Basketball. And if that's not who you are inside, then it's not you they're liking. So what's the point? Still, I don't mind playing, just not all the time.

This year is looking better. My English teacher has got us studying the Harlem Renaissance, which means we have to read a lot of poetry. That suits me just fine, gives me a reason to drag around my beat-up volumes of Langston Hughes and Claude McKay. Whenever anybody bugs me about it, all I have to say is "Homework." Even so, I'd rather the brothers not catch me with my head in a book. ❸

The other day, I duck into the library, snare a corner table, and hunker down with *3000 Years of Black Poetry*. Raynard sees me, but it's not like he's going to tell anybody. He hardly speaks, and he never hangs with any of the brothers I know. So I breathe easy. I'm sure no one else has spotted me until a head pops up from behind the stacks. It's Janelle Battle from my English class. I freeze and wait for the snickers I'm used to. Wait for her to say something like: "What? Coach got you *reading* now? Afraid you're gonna flunk out and drop off the team?" But all she does is smile and wave. Like it's no big deal for me to be in a library reading. Like I have a right to be there if I want. Then she pads over, slips a copy of *The Panther & the Lash* on my table, and walks away without saying a word. It's one of my favorite books by Langston Hughes. How could she know? Seems like she's noticed me in the library more often than I thought.

**❸ Making Inferences**
Why doesn't Devon want his friends to catch him reading a book?

Janelle is all right. So what if she's a little plump? At least when you turn the light on upstairs, somebody's at home. She's smart, and she doesn't try hiding it. Which gets me thinking. Maybe it's time I quit sneaking in and out of the library like some thief. Maybe it's time I just started being who I am.

# Bronx Masquerade

## by Devon Hope

I woke up this morning
exhausted from hiding
the me of me
so I stand here confiding
there's more to Devon
than jump shot and rim.
I'm more than tall
and lengthy of limb.
I dare you to peep
behind these eyes,
discover the poet
in tough-guy disguise.
Don't call me Jump Shot.
My name is Surprise. ○

## Answering the BIG Question

As you do the following activities, consider the Big Question:
**How do you stay true to yourself?**

**WRITE TO LEARN** Think about the three essays you have read in this selection. What did you learn about staying true to yourself? Write down your thoughts in a brief entry in your Learner's Notebook.

**LITERATURE GROUPS** Meet with two or three others who have read the excerpts from *Bronx Masquerade*. Discuss the "masks" that people sometimes wear and why it can be hard for people to reveal their true selves.

# 5 Clever Survivors

## The extraordinary ways animals heal themselves

by Aline Alexander Newman

**Find out about the surprising survival strategies of five different animals.**

JoJo, a wild male bottlenose dolphin, was throwing up and Dean Bernal was worried. The <u>naturalist</u> and diver had never seen

## Vo•cab•u•lary

**naturalist** (NACH ur uh list) a scientist who studies plants and animals a dolphin do this. Was the animal sick? Would he be OK?

Dean Bernal, of Aptos, California, knows this dolphin well. He watched as JoJo <u>zoomed</u> through the waves with his mouth wide open. The dolphin gulped down so much seawater that "his throat swelled up like a pelican's pouch." Then the dolphin threw up again.

Using a fine mesh screen and a plastic jar, Bernal collected the dolphin's stomach contents to have them <u>analyzed</u>. And when he did—good news! JoJo wasn't sick at all. In fact, Bernal concluded the dolphin was preventing himself from getting ill.

In the wild, dolphins eat what they can find, which sometimes includes big fish such as groupers and flounders. "The dolphins' stomachs can't digest those huge bones," says Bernal. "So wild dolphins swallow lots of water to help flush out the bones." (<u>Captive</u> dolphins don't <u>regurgitate</u> because they're fed small-boned fish such as herring.)

Scientists recently came up with a name for this kind of behavior. "It's called 'animal self-medication,'" says wildlife biologist Michael Huffman of Kyoto University, in Japan. "It includes all the things wild animals do to help themselves—and sometimes each other—stay healthy or get better when they're hurt or sick." ❶

❶ **Questioning**
What is "animal self-medication"?

You'll be amazed at the <u>ingenious</u> tricks animal "doctors" have <u>conjured</u> up to help them stay fit!

---

## Vo•cab•u•lary

**zoomed** (zoomd) moved quickly
**analyzed** (AN uh lyzd) tested or examined
**captive** (KAP tiv) an animal or person that is confined
**regurgitate** (ree GUR juh tayt) to throw up
**ingenious** (in JEEN yus) clever and imaginative
**conjured** (KON jurd) came up with as if by magic or special powers

### Bug Off

When Hi, a wedge-capped capuchin monkey, found a <u>millipede</u>, biologist John Robinson thought the bug had just become monkey chow. He was studying the monkeys in the forests of Venezuela. Robinson expected the female monkey to gobble it up as she would a cricket or a grasshopper. She didn't. Hi simply put the millipede in her mouth and bit it gently. Then she rubbed it all over her body, much like you would use sunscreen. And that's not all. When Hi finished using it, she passed the millipede to another monkey, who did the same thing. "What's going on here?" Robinson wondered.

"Chewing on the millipede obviously caused it to release some kind of chemical," says Robinson. But he didn't know what kind, so he sent the millipede to a lab to be analyzed. The conclusion? Millipedes produce a powerful insect repellent. The monkeys look for millipedes most often during the rainy season, when pesky mosquitoes are at their worst. What a perfect way to tell the pests to bug off!

### Forest Pharmacy

The WaTongwe people were sick, and their medicine man couldn't heal them—until a porcupine led him to the cure! Frustrated that none of his traditional medicines were working to ease a terrible intestinal illness people were

### Vo•cab•u•lary

**millipede** (MIL ih peed) a crawling insect

suffering, Babu Kalunde went hunting. While in the forest near Lake Tanganyika, in Africa, he happened upon an orphaned baby crested porcupine. Kalunde rescued it, but then his prickly pet developed the same symptoms as the sick villagers.

Believing that animals could doctor themselves, Kalunde let the porcupine return to the woods. He watched as the creature ignored its usual foods and instead chewed on the roots of a mulengelele plant. Two days later, the porcupine was back to normal.

Kalunde used mulengelele to create a new medicine to give his patients. It worked! "Mulengelele is now being used by people throughout western Tanzania," says Huffman. Leave it to a porcupine to make a good point!

## Open Wide!

Belle, a captive chimpanzee, never went to dental school. But she certainly knew all about teeth. "The chimps in Belle's group did lots of bark chewing," says Miami University professor William C. McGrew of Oxford, Ohio. "They'd get pieces of bark caught between their teeth." One day Belle was cleaning the teeth of a young chimp named Shadow when she discovered a loose one.

Belle wiggled the baby tooth back and forth. It stayed put. She grabbed hold and pulled. Still nothing happened. This called for desperate measures! Belle reached for the "tool kit" that she kept on a platform in her enclosure—a collection of sticks ranging from the size of a toothpick to as big as a chisel. "Dr. Belle" selected one and poked it under the loose tooth. Then, *ouch!* She pried it out. "Shadow could have closed his mouth anytime," says McGrew. "But he cooperated." Why? Either the tooth hurt, or Shadow hoped the tooth fairy would leave a banana under his pillow.

## Fever Buster

Yoda's nose was swollen up like a balloon. The wild black bear had been fighting with another bear over who controlled certain territory, and she got clawed on the nose. The scratch became infected, and now Yoda's body was burning hot with fever.

"I think she recognized that she had a problem," says wildlife biologist Ben Kilham of Lyme Center, New Hampshire. Kilham, who studies bears, watched as Yoda nursed herself back to health. First she <u>lumbered</u> into a swamp. Then she used her front paws to dig a hole on a little rise underneath the roots of a tree. Finally, she crawled into this soggy den to rest.

"This was very abnormal behavior," says Kilham. Bears usually dig dens where it's dry. But this cold, wet hole may have helped bring Yoda's temperature down. When she crawled back out, the swelling had begun to <u>subside</u> and Yoda acted fine. That's one chilled-out bear! ○

## Answering the BIG Question

As you do the following activities, consider the Big Question:
**How do you stay true to yourself?**

**WRITE TO LEARN** Think about how these animals came up with ways to heal themselves and stay healthy. Write a brief entry in your Learner's Notebook about an animal you know and how it acts when it is sick or injured.

**PARTNER TALK** Meet with another student who has read this selection. Imagine you are going to do an informational video about one of these animals. Which would you select and why? What would you show in your video?

## Vo•cab•u•lary

**lumbered** (LUM burd) moved clumsily
**subside** (sub SYD) go down; decrease

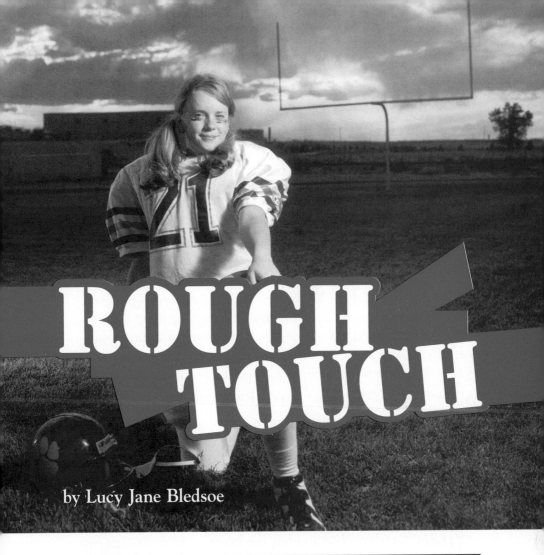

# ROUGH TOUCH

by Lucy Jane Bledsoe

---

**How do you stay true to yourself when there's pressure to be something you're not?**

---

**R**uthie wasn't hungry for breakfast. She dreaded her race that afternoon. She hated track and field. It was the worst sport. You're by yourself. They see you. They see all of you. They see you come in last. In a race, there was only a starting line, running bodies, and a finish line. There was no way to lose yourself. **❶**

> **❶ Predicting**
> What do you think this story will be about?

"You have to eat," her mom said, so Ruthie poured the skim milk on her sugarless cereal and looked into the bowl.

"Which event are you doing?" her mom asked too cheerfully.

"Fifteen hundred meter." Those three words felt like icy stones in Ruthie's mouth.

"You should be running the hundred meter. You have sprinter's genes."

Ruthie's mom had been saying this every day all fall. *You have sprinter's genes.* Without even looking, Ruthie could see her mom's blue ribbons billowing, as if they were flag sized, in the glass cabinet behind the kitchen table. She could also picture perfectly the photograph next to the ribbons, her mom's arms raised over her head as her chest busted through the finish-line tape. She could see her mom's short hair, wet with sweat and victory, her long limbs, stringy with perfectly tuned muscles.

"I want to quit the track team," Ruthie said.

"Oh, honey." Her mom softened and began rebraiding Ruthie's hair. "Give it one season. By the end of the year, you'll love running. You'll feel so good about yourself once you slim down."

Her mother finally went upstairs to dress for work, and Ruthie dumped her soggy cereal down the garbage disposal. She grabbed her gym bag and left the house without saying good-bye, slamming the door. ❷ As she walked to school, she crawled deep into her body, as if it were a cave where she could hide. Inside there, she could be anyone she wanted to be. Inside there, she could wander for hours and no one would bother her. Sometimes she liked that feeling, but other times she felt too alone.

> ❷ **Making Inferences**
> Why does Ruthie leave the house in this manner?

## Vo•cab•u•lary

**genes** (jeens) parts of the cells passed on by parents to their children that determine how they look and grow
**billowing** (BIL oh ing) pushed outward by the wind

She wanted out and couldn't find the passageway.

Ruthie kicked the crispy brown and yellow leaves as she walked, hoping for a miracle that would cancel the track-and-field meet. A <u>torrential</u> storm. A massive traffic jam that prevented the other team from getting to her school. Maybe she could sprain her ankle.

None of those things happened, though, by the time she reached the entrance to her school. As she entered the building, Ruthie pressed her books against her chest as if they were a football. She pretended the hallway was a field, a hundred yards long and fifty wide. All the kids pushing toward her, shoving past her, were her opponents. The door of her classroom was the goal line. If she could get there without <u>encountering</u> Joel Woodbridge, she would score a touchdown.

When her classroom was just ten yards away, she thought of raising her books over her head and prancing, her knees high, like the pros did when they crossed the goal line for a touchdown. It wouldn't matter if she did that. Everyone already

---

### Vo•cab•u•lary

**torrential** (tor REN shul) flowing in great quantities
**encountering** (en KOWN tur ing) running into; meeting

thought she was weird. But she kept the books plastered to her chest. She kept moving down the hall. Five yards to go. Three yards.

Joel Woodbridge blocked her way. "Boom!" he said. "Flat on their faces. Come on, Ruthie. You'd be the best tackle in the school."

Every day a group of boys played pickup football after school. And every day Joel asked Ruthie to block for him. Of course, he was <u>taunting</u> her, making fun of her being fat, but he always said it as a mock compliment. "You'd be awesome. No one could get around you."

Usually when Ruthie saw Joel's white-blond head and jutting red ears coming down the hall, she tried to avoid him. No one could stand Joel. He was mean. He enjoyed annoying people. He was always smart-mouthing. Ruthie didn't want anyone to think that she was friends with him. But here was the problem: Joel shared her passion for football. Sometimes, even though she knew he was taunting her, even though she knew they probably wouldn't really let her, she considered his offer to play football with the boys. She wanted to play so badly. The mud and grass stains. The hard, cold air. The rough touch. ❸

Today he stood in her path, his eyes all wild and flashing, and asked her, "Hey, Ruthie, did ya see that play last night?"

❸ **Predicting**
Do you think Ruthie will play football with the boys?

She couldn't help smiling. It was that perfect forty-three-yard pass that won the game for the Niners. Unfortunately, right after the quarterback hauled back his arm and let fly, her mother appeared in the doorway of the family room and began nagging her about eating Red Vines the night before a track meet. "Shhh," Ruthie had said as she watched the spiraling football reach the <u>apex</u> of its flight. She

## Vo•cab•u•lary

**taunting** (TAWNT ing) teasing in a nasty way
**apex** (AY peks) the highest point

loved the way it looked against the cold night sky and then, as it began to <u>descend</u>, against the bright green Astroturf. She loved watching the fluid legs of the wide receiver run toward the ball's destination. The way his hands reached out, just barely catching the pass the second after he crossed the goal line. She loved the roaring fans, the team hugs, the commentators' pumped-up voices. She loved the slow-motion instant replays.

"Ruthie, I'm *talking* to you," her mother said two more times.

If only Ruthie could disappear into that perfect pass and catch. If only, for just a moment even, she could *become* that perfectly spinning football.

That was the thing about Joel Woodbridge. He was <u>obnoxious</u>. But he understood *that* about football. Still, she didn't want anyone seeing her talking to Joel. So she stepped around him and entered the classroom.

"Ka-*boom*," he said to her back. "You'd flatten the whole defense."

After school, Ruthie walked slowly to the track for her meet. A few minutes later, she stood on the starting line with the other girls. The sky was dark, almost purple, and an irregular wind tossed a hamburger carton across the runners' lanes. The starting gun fired. Cold air raked her lungs as she ran. She knew she should find a pace she could <u>sustain</u> for the whole fifteen hundred meters. But if she went fast now, she could feel, for about a hundred meters anyway, like a real runner. A fast runner. Someone with sprinter's genes.

Then she fell behind. Way behind.

Still, Ruthie ran. She ran as fast as she could. She ran until she felt as if a knife were <u>lodged</u> in her side. She ran until she felt nauseous. She ran until she crossed the finish line, last, so

---

## Vo·cab·u·lary

**descend** (dih SEND) go down
**obnoxious** (ub NAWK shus) annoying and offensive
**sustain** (suh STAYN) to maintain; to keep going
**lodged** (lojd) stuck

far behind the other girls that the parents had already <u>surged</u> down to the track to hug their winning daughters. Ruthie had to push through the small crowd to finish the race.

She didn't stop running then, either. She ran right out of the track gates and up to the top of the hill. Finally, panting, she collapsed on the grass. In the distance, on the lower field that was full of potholes and weeds, Joel and his friends had already begun playing football. All Ruthie wanted was to wipe out the feeling of that race, to <u>annihilate</u> the picture of <u>jubilant</u> parents hugging their fast, slim daughters. After catching her breath, she stood up and walked down to the lower field.

"I'll block for you," she told Joel.

He looked surprised, so taken off guard that he didn't smart-mouth anything, only said, "Okay."

Some of the other boys grumbled. A couple of them laughed. But in fact, Joel's team was one player short. So they shrugged, and someone said, "As long as she doesn't get in the way."

But Ruthie knew exactly what to do. She had studied the players' moves on TV. She blocked for Joel. She took the hits. She was good at it, too, and Joel ran twenty-two yards, then another ten. On fourth down, he scored a touchdown. ❹

> ❹ **Questioning**
> How does Ruthie perform when she joins the team?

Ruthie's arms, legs, and sides hurt, but the ache felt good. With football, there's a reason for running. There's wind and mud. The autumny smell of grass. The tangle of bodies. Her own body became part of a big strategy, bigger even than the game she was playing. It was as if she had not only found the passageway out of the cave, but blown the top off.

When her team got the ball again, Ruthie spoke up in the

---

## Vo•cab•u•lary

**surged** (surjd) moved forward forcefully
**annihilate** (uh NY uh layt) to destroy completely
**jubilant** (JOO buh lunt) delighted; very happy

huddle. "I want to go deep this time. Joel, let someone block for *me*."

"As if," one boy said.

"Oh, yeah right," another groaned.

"Let's do it!" Joel piped up, flashing his devil grin, the one the teachers hated. "It'll totally throw them off. They'll never expect it."

Joel dropped to his knees and used his finger to draw imaginary lines on the grass. He showed Ruthie where to begin blocking for him, as a fake, and then where to take off running long. The quarterback would hand off to Joel. He would fake as if he were going to run but quickly lateral the ball back to the quarterback, who would pass to Ruthie.

It had been her idea, but now she shook her head. Her legs ached from running. Her chest hurt from taking hits and from sucking the cold air. Being a receiver was very different from blocking.

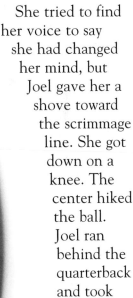

She tried to find her voice to say she had changed her mind, but Joel gave her a shove toward the scrimmage line. She got down on a knee. The center hiked the ball. Joel ran behind the quarterback and took the handoff. That's when Ruthie felt her entire body <u>rivet</u> to attention. She didn't even have to think. She blocked for Joel, pushing aside two boys, then took off running long.

Ruthie wasn't fast, but she surprised the boys. For a few moments, no one took off after her. She turned to look for the pass, and there it was. A perfect spiral heading her way. Ruthie panicked. The ball was coming fast. She pushed her legs to go faster, stretch longer.

She lifted her arms and reached, just like the Niners' wide receiver. Her fingers touched the ball, and she gripped. It was hers, the football was hers.

Ruthie ran. Joel had caught up to her and was now at her side, sweeping the field, clearing her path. But the pack of boys was gaining on her, and he couldn't handle all of them. One dove at her legs. He wrapped his arms around her ankles. She tried to

## Vo•cab•u•lary

**rivet** (RIV it) to completely capture one's attention

kick him off, but she was going down.

"Reach!" Joel shouted as she fell. So she did. She reached her arms in front of her, thrusting the football across the end-zone line as her face slammed into the hard, weedy ground.

Joel shot both arms high and parallel in the air. "Touchdown!" he shouted.

Then he dropped to his knees beside Ruthie and gently touched her cheekbone where a bruise would soon appear. "You okay?" he asked. She rolled over on her side and looked up at him. Briefly she saw the face of a boy who loved football more than he loved being mean. She fought back her <u>welling</u> tears, conquered them, and jumped to her feet.

A moment later, Ruthie was on the line of scrimmage, ready to play defense. **5** ○

> **5 Analyzing**
> What is the main idea, or message, of this story?

---

## Answering the
## **BIG** Question

As you do the following activities, consider the Big Question:
**How do you stay true to yourself?**

**WRITE TO LEARN** Think about how Ruthie was on the track team because her mother wanted her to be a runner. Write a brief entry in your Learner's Notebook about a time when you did something to please someone else and not because it was what you wanted.

**LITERATURE GROUPS** Meet with two or three classmates who have read "Rough Touch." Discuss how it is sometimes hard for teens to follow their own interests instead of doing what other people think they should do.

---

### Vo•cab•u•lary

**welling** (WEL ing) rising to the surface, ready to flow

# COACH'S SON

by Kathi Appelt

**There's more to the coach's son than meets the eye.**

He's tall
almost six feet
broad shoulders
good for carrying
the football
the load
the cheers
one hundred ninety pounds
he'll be a starter on the
varsity team next year
he'll need a tutor in math
he'd like to play the trombone
he loves to play Nintendo
he can play any position
all positions
but the hardest—
coach's son ❶
his secret—
how much he loves
to hear his mama sing to him
…rock-a-bye, my sleepy boy…
as he drifts off to sleep.

❶ **Making Inferences**
Why is the position of "coach's son" the hardest one to play?

# Poem for My Sister

by Liz Lochhead

---

**An older sister gives some advice.**

---

My little sister likes to try my shoes,
to strut in them,
admire her spindle-thin twelve-year-old legs
in this season's styles.
She says they fit her perfectly,
but wobbles
on their high heels, they're
hard to balance.

I like to watch my little sister
playing hopscotch, admire the neat hops-and-skips of her,
their quick peck,
never-missing their mark, not
over-stepping the line.
She is competent at peever.

**23**

I try to warn my little sister
About unsuitable shoes,
point out my own <u>distorted</u> feet,
the <u>callouses</u>,
odd patches of hard skin.
I should not like to see her
in my shoes.
I wish she could stay
sure footed,
sensibly <u>shod</u>. ❷ ○

> ❷ **Making Inferences**
> Do you think the speaker is talking about more than just shoes? Explain.

## Answering the BIG Question

As you do the following activities, consider the Big Question:
**How do you stay true to yourself?**

**WRITE TO LEARN** Imagine yourself in a variety of footwear: slippers, boots, shoes, or sandals. Write a brief entry in your Learner's Notebook describing the footwear that seems most like you.

**PARTNER TALK** Get together with a partner who has read these poems. Discuss the hopes and expectations that others have for the coach's son and the little sister.

## Vo•cab•u•lary

**distorted** (dis TORT id) twisted or changed
**callouses** (KAL us es) tough or hard skin
**shod** (shod) wearing shoes

# NO CHEERS FOR ME!!

by Cathryn Hahn

GO-O-O-O LAKESIDE!!

RAH! RAH! RAH!

**Staying true to yourself is hard when your best friend wants you to be something you're not.**

THIS WASN'T SUPPOSED TO HAPPEN.

DID YOU HEAR? YOU BOTH MADE THE SQUAD!

SWEET!

WHY DID THEY PICK ME? I HATE CHEERING.

ISN'T THIS *GREAT*, TISHA?

UH ... YEAH. GREAT.

THEY WERE SUPPOSED TO REJECT ME ... SO I WOULDN'T HAVE TO TELL RAINA.

I'VE ALWAYS GONE ALONG WITH HER SCHEMES, LIKE HOW WE STOLE HER SISTER'S MAKEUP BOX ...

*AUGH!* RAINA! WHAT ARE YOU *DOING?*

HEE HEE

GIGGLE

... OR WHEN WE TRIED TO BUST LOOSE FROM THE FIFTH-GRADE FIELD TRIP.

WE'LL DUCK AROUND THIS CORNER AS SOON AS NO ONE'S LOOKING.

YEAH, I'VE PRETTY MUCH ALWAYS DONE WHATEVER RAINA WANTS TO DO.

WE'RE GOING TO BE THE HOTTEST CHEERLEADERS IN SCHOOL!

UH-HUH.

PRACTICE TURNED OUT TO BE PRETTY AWFUL.

LETICIA! C'MON, GIRL! KEEP IN STEP!

IT'S RIGHT – RIGHT – LEFT, LETICIA!

OKAY, TEN MINUTE BREAK!

WHAT'S UP, TISH? YOU WERE DOING GREAT AT TRYOUTS.

I DON'T KNOW, RAINS. JUST NERVOUS, I GUESS.

NERVOUS?! WHAT DO YOU HAVE TO BE NERVOUS ABOUT?

NOTHING. I DON'T KNOW.

I WASN'T REALLY MESSING UP ON PURPOSE. I JUST COULDN'T CONCENTRATE.

C'MON, GRACEFUL. BREAK'S OVER.

I SURE WAS HAPPY TO SEE MY MOM WHEN PRACTICE WAS OVER.

MY MOM'S HERE – GOTTA GO! BYE!

HOW WAS PRACTICE, HONEY?

NOT SO GOOD. I DON'T THINK I LIKE CHEERING.

WHAT DO YOU MEAN? I THOUGHT YOU WERE EXCITED TO JOIN THE SQUAD.

I THOUGHT I WAS TOO, AT FIRST. RAINA'S THE ONE WHO'S EXCITED ABOUT IT.

I KEPT MESSING UP TODAY. THE COACH WAS YELLING AT ME MORE THAN ANYONE.

OH, SWEETIE. JUST STICK WITH IT. YOU'LL GET BETTER WITH TIME.

BUT MOM ... I DON'T *WANT* TO DO IT! I FEEL STUPID CHEERING. IT'S NOT *ME!*

IT FEELS PHONY ... LIKE I'M TRYING TO BE SOMEONE I'M NOT.

OH, TISHA. IT'S JUST BECAUSE YOU'RE SO SHY. IT'LL BE GOOD FOR YOU.

SOMETIMES I WONDER IF MY MOM WISHES SHE COULD TRADE ME IN FOR RAINA.

BESIDES, IT'LL BE A FUN THING TO DO WITH RAINA.

MAYBE THEY HAVE MORE IN COMMON WITH EACH OTHER THAN WITH ME.

I WISH I HAD SOMEONE ELSE TO TALK WITH ABOUT THIS.

IF THIS WASN'T ABOUT RAINA, I'D BE ON THE PHONE WITH HER RIGHT NOW.

RAINA'S BEEN TALKING ABOUT TRYING OUT FOR CHEERLEADING SINCE FOURTH GRADE!

BACK THEN IT SOUNDED GREAT. BUT WHAT ABOUT WHAT I'M INTO? RAINA NEVER MENTIONED THE SHORT STORY I WROTE.

BUT SHE'S MY BEST FRIEND. I'M MAKING HER OUT LIKE SHE'S A JERK, BUT SHE'S BEEN THERE FOR ME A LOT.

I DON'T KNOW HOW I'M GOING TO TALK TO RAINA ABOUT THIS.

I KNOW IT SOUNDS STUPID. IF WE'RE SUCH GOOD FRIENDS, SHE SHOULD UNDERSTAND, RIGHT?

I KNEW SHE'D BE LIKE THIS. THAT GIRL MAKES ME SO MAD SOMETIMES. WELL, AT LEAST I GOT THAT OVER WITH . . .

... AND NOW I HAVE SOME TIME TO CHECK OUT SOMETHING I'VE BEEN THINKING ABOUT!

THE LAKESIDE LEDGER
WANTS YOU!
WRITE FOR THE SCHOOL PAPER!

I NEEDED SOME SPACE FROM RAINA FOR A WHILE, BUT WE WORKED IT OUT. EVER SINCE I STARTED WRITING FOR THE LAKESIDE LEDGER EVERYTHING'S BEEN GREAT. I COVER ALL THE GAMES, SO RAINA AND I USUALLY END UP HANGING OUT AFTERWARDS.

NEW CHEER SQUAD HAS SPIRIT TO SPARE!

**WRITE TO LEARN**
What do you think will happen next? In your Learner's Notebook, draw a few panels, or cells, to tell what happens now that Tisha is free to do her own thing. Include dialogue.

*from* **What Are You? Voices of Mixed-Race Young People**

# My Look Says Nothing About Who I Am

by Michael Logan

**If you could not see what a person looked like, would that change the way you react to him or her?**

**W**hat I like most is that my look says nothing about who I am. There are <u>stereotypes</u> of Asians, blacks, whites, Hispanics, et cetera. When you look at me, you can't tell what I am. I think it's positive in the sense that, when somebody doesn't know what you are, they don't bring whatever <u>prejudices</u> they have into their <u>interaction</u> with you.

Also, what is it to be one person who's two things? People don't know what that is. They don't get any information about mixed-race people from the media, and chances are, they know few others.

## Vo·cab·u·lary

**stereotypes** (STAIR ee oh typs) overly simple opinions or images of a group of people
**prejudices** (PREJ uh dis es) unfair opinions based on a characteristic, such as a person's race or appearance
**interaction** (in tur AKT shun) an involvement or encounter

## My Look Says Nothing About Who I Am

People don't readily <u>dismiss</u> me based on their own stereotypes, because I don't fit within the <u>framework</u> of their knowledge. They don't say, "He is Asian, and here is what I know about Asians, and so here is how I must interact with him." So they want to find out, "Who is this person?" And that means they get past the looks to find out about me. They have to put in a little bit more work to get to know who I am. **❶**

> **❶ Questioning**
> What does Michael like about his looks?

## Vo•cab•u•lary

**dismiss** (dis MIS) to stop thinking about something; to put something out of mind

**framework** (FRAYM wurk) structure

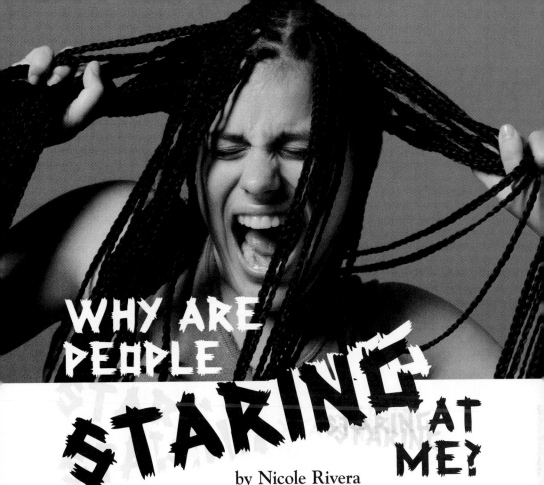

# WHY ARE PEOPLE STARING AT ME?

## by Nicole Rivera

**W**hen I was in second grade, this little boy—he was Argentinian—invited me to his birthday party. I went and I had fun, and my mom came to pick me up. Well, the next day in school he goes, "I would have never invited you to my birthday party if I had known you were black." And I punched him.

I couldn't imagine that coming out of somebody's mouth who is that small. His parents must have said something.

I don't have the same skin color as my mother—she has darker skin. When I go to the store with her, the salesperson will go, "Are you together?" Or, "Next."

My dad is light-skinned. So my friends always ask me, "Is your dad white?"

# Why Are People Staring at Me?

My hair throws people off too. People are always looking at my hair trying to figure out what I am. I have really thick black hair. I use black hair products and I only go to black hairdressers. People are always like, "Wait a minute. She's light-skinned, but look at her hair!"

I get mad because people are always trying to <u>categorize</u> me. People try to figure me out like I'm some puzzle. That's really annoying. I can understand that people are curious, but they ask me questions all the time. Why can't they leave me alone? I am what I am. I really respect the people who get to know me first and ask me later.

But the people who come up to me and say, "What are you?"—I have no clue why they want to know. There's a group of black girls at my high school, and they'll always make <u>snide</u> comments to me. They'll go, "What are you? Are you white and black? Are you Indian?" Just the way they ask is <u>obnoxious</u> too. It's kind of like, "What are you—you alien?" They're poking and probing.

Sometimes they're like, "Look at that black girl trying to act white." Or, "Look at that Puerto Rican girl trying to act black." My boyfriend is black, and sometimes when I walk down the hall with him, they say, "Why is he going out with that white girl?" Maybe he's going out with me because he likes me. You learn to brush it off, because people are just ignorant.

Ignorance is fear of the unknown. If you're ignorant about something, then you're scared of it. Well, I'm not scared of Latino people and I'm not scared of black people. I feel lucky to know both sides. I'm a more open-minded individual because of that. I have friends who are white, and I have friends who are Puerto Rican, friends from Colombia, friends who are black.

I'm lucky because I have two cultures instead of just one. My

---

## Vo•cab•u•lary

**categorize** (KAT ih gor ryz) to put into groups
**snide** (snyd) unpleasant in a mean-spirited way
**obnoxious** (ub NAWK shus) annoying and offensive

dad never taught me Spanish, but I hang out with my friends who are Puerto Rican and I pick up things from them. And I listen to salsa and merengue. And I listen to R&B and rap. I eat Hispanic food and I listen to the Spanish radio station.

But at the same time, being both has kind of made me self-conscious. People see me in so many different ways. So I'm never sure if people are treating me a certain way because of what I look like or because of who I am. Something will happen and I'll be like, "Is this a racial thing? Or is it just because they don't like me?"

I'll say to my boyfriend, "Why are people staring at me, trying to figure out what I am?"

He'll say, "How do you know they're not just saying, 'Oh, wow, that's a nice shirt,' or 'I like her hair'?" Sometimes I think he's right. But I feel like I'm not understood sometimes. He's trying to understand, but you can't understand it unless you've experienced it. ❷

People are ignorant, you know. Maybe eventually they'll learn—when everyone is the same shade of gray. ○

❷ **Questioning**
How do Nicole's experiences affect the way she reacts to people?

## Answering the BIG Question

As you do the following activities, consider the Big Question:
**How do you stay true to yourself?**

**WRITE TO LEARN** Think about the writers' experiences described in these selections. Write a brief entry in your Learner's Notebook reflecting on how people form opinions of other people based on their looks.

**LITERATURE GROUPS** Meet with two or three others who have read the excerpts from *What Are You?* Discuss experiences you have had or have observed that are similar to those described by the writers.

# Being Indian

by Dana Mathias (Tohono O'odham)
*Grade 8; age 14; Baboquivari High School, Sells, Arizona*

**A young poet shares her feelings about being herself.**

Being Indian is being proud
and happy for who you are.
Dark skin and dark hair
that make the white man stare.
Living in a village
with your relatives
making sure the desert still lives.
Keeping your head up
making sure no one
lets you down
'cause you're too proud
of who you are
'cause you're Indian.

# THOUGHTS OF THE DIFFERENT

### by Adi Givati, 14

**One poet dares to be different.**

Why? You ask why?
Why I choose to be an outsider?
Well first of all when you choose
You're not really an outsider
Second, because that's the way I am.
Crowds make me uncomfortable,
I don't like to dance
I don't like *their* groups
I don't understand *them, their* language
I don't understand *them,* and you know what?
I don't want to.
I don't want to because, I think if I did
I wouldn't be the way I am.
Happy.
And if I changed to the point where I *do* understand *them*
I think I'd die
That's all and that's why.  ○

## Answering the BIG Question

As you do the following activities, consider the Big Question:
**How do you stay true to yourself?**

**WRITE TO LEARN** Think about how both poems reveal something important about the speaker's personality or life. In your Learner's Notebook, write a short poem about an aspect of your life or personality that's important to you. You can model your poem on one of the poems on these pages.

**LITERATURE GROUPS** Meet with two or three others who have read these poems. Discuss the tone of each poem and what makes the speaker special. Talk about how their attitudes are similar and different.

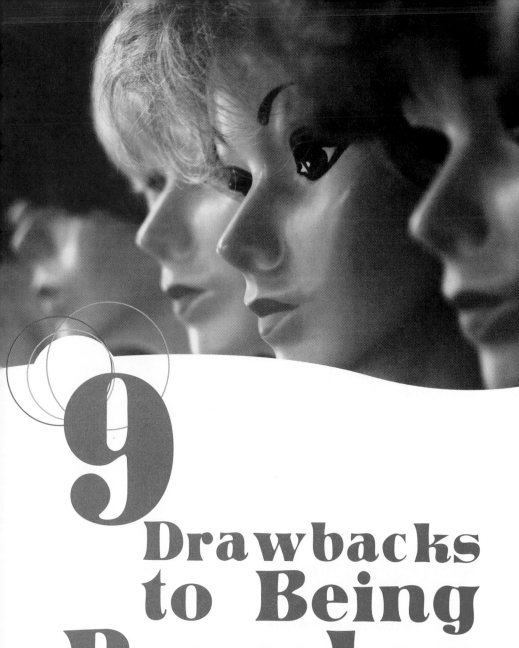

# 9 Drawbacks to Being Popular

by Sandra and Harry Choron

Being popular may not be as great as you think!

**E**very teen wants to be popular, and one of the biggest pressures in your life will be in meeting the expectations of friends and peers just to stay popular. But popularity can backfire. Read this list, then ask yourself how important popularity really is to you. **❶**

**❶ Predicting**
Will you change your opinion of popularity after reading this list?

1. A lot of teens, in attempting to be popular, often can't be themselves around their friends. They wind up feeling pressured to act a certain way just to be liked. They lose out because in the end, people who can't show others who they really are don't have many real friends.

2. Popular kids often feel like they've got to go along with the crowd to stay popular, so they wind up saying "Sure" when they really mean "No way!" This can get dangerous.

3. In order to maintain their popularity, some teens act tough and encourage others to be the same way. Often, they'll find someone or some group to pick on. This is how a gang mentality develops.

4. Some teens use drugs or alcohol to stay popular.

5. Some teens sacrifice their self-esteem and possibly their safety by having sex because they believe "everyone's doing it."

6. Popular teens often hide their real emotions and pretend to be happy when they are really sad. They're afraid to express their real emotions because everyone expects them to be happy and in control.

---

### Vo•cab•u•lary

**backfire** (BAK fyr) create an unintended result
**mentality** (men TAL uh tee) mental attitude
**self-esteem** (self uh STEEM) a feeling of pride in oneself

7. Some teen girls develop serious eating disorders because they feel that they must be thin to be popular.

8. Keeping up with the latest fashion trends to be popular can be stressful and expensive.

9. Popular teens often make friends with other teens just because they too are popular. Often they don't really enjoy those people or have real bonds with them. ❷ ○

❷ **Questioning**
What are some examples of how popularity can backfire?

---

## Answering the BIG Question

As you do the following activities, consider the Big Question:
**How do you stay true to yourself?**

**WRITE TO LEARN** Did reading this article change your opinion about popularity? Do you think it's possible to stay popular and also stay true to yourself? Answer these questions in a brief entry in your Learner's Notebook.

**LITERATURE GROUPS** Meet with two or three others who have read this selection. Discuss the drawbacks to being popular that the authors have listed. Can your group think of other drawbacks? You may want to compare your ideas with another group.

# KEEP STARING: I MIGHT DO A TRICK!

by Willem Winkelman
as told to Rachel Buchholz

**Willem Winkelman is here to tell you that you can't judge a book by its cover.**

That's the message on a T-shirt of mine. People stare at me all the time, so I thought this shirt would be funny. See, I'm a dwarf.

Most of the time people aren't trying to be rude—they just haven't seen many dwarfs like me before. I can understand that. But I also want to let them know that I see them staring. Usually the T-shirt makes them laugh at themselves, not at me.

## Big Challenges

I was born with achondroplasia (ah-con-droh-PLAY-sha), the most common form of dwarfism. I have an average-size <u>torso</u>, but my arms and legs are shorter and my head is bigger than average.

Right now I'm almost four feet tall, and that's about as tall as I'm going to get. I'm not going to pretend that my height isn't a challenge. It is. Light switches and counters are usually too high for me. I can't reach some shelves in the grocery stores. It takes me three steps to keep up with one step of an average-size adult. And my mom has to hem almost all of my pants.

But everyone faces challenges. You just have to face them with a good attitude. So I have a long barbecue fork to pull things down from pantry shelves. I'm a great climber, and I can make a stool out of just about anything. I'll even be able to drive a car, with the help of pedal extensions. If all else fails, I ask for help.

The way I see it, I can do just about anything that an average-size person can do. OK, so I'll never play professional sports, but I have no problem testing my limits. I have to. For instance, everyone uses stoves. Little people just have to figure out how to use them in different ways. (I use a stool to reach mine at home.) It may take me longer, and it may be harder, but I can still do it. ❶

> **❶ Questioning**
> How does Willem deal with the challenges he faces?

## Stare-Off

The hardest thing about being a dwarf is dealing with people's reactions. Sometimes people seem to think I'm invisible, and they'll do stuff like cut in front of me in a line, as if I'm not even there. And one time I was with about five of my dwarf friends, and this woman wanted to take our picture! We said no, but she kept asking. It was like she thought we were street performers or something!

---

## Vo•cab•u•lary

**torso** (TOR soh) the part of a person's body between the neck and waist, not including the arms

My average-size friends will stick up for me, like when there's a new kid at school who's making fun of me. If I'm with my dwarf friends, mostly we just ignore the stares and the teasing. Sometimes we'll stare back—hard—and that usually embarrasses the person so much that the staring stops.

Except for rude people, I don't want to make anyone uncomfortable. So I don't mind some questions. Usually people want to know what to call a person with my condition. I tell them it's OK to refer to people like me as dwarfs or little people. Just don't call us midgets—it's an outdated term that offends us. I don't mind talking about dwarfism, because that makes people see I'm a person just like them.

My T-shirt kind of does the same thing: It shows people the real me, a kid with a sense of humor. And maybe that's the real trick: showing others that I'm just like them. I play sports and video games, I go to school, and I hang out with my friends. I'm just shorter. I mean, no one is exactly the same. We're all different in some way, so we should just accept each other's differences. And anyway, I'm proud of who I am. Why would I want to change? ○

*Thirteen-year-old dwarf Daniel Torres proudly holds the football on the Thomas A. Edison Middle School team.*

## Answering the BIG Question

As you do the following activities, consider the Big Question:
**How do you stay true to yourself?**

**WRITE TO LEARN** Think about how people stare at Willem or treat him rudely. In your Learner's Notebook describe a time when someone has stared at you or made you feel uncomfortable. How did you react?

**PARTNER TALK** Meet with another student who has read this selection. Discuss how Willem uses his T-shirt to send a message to people who stare at him. Think of other peaceful ways to deal with rude, insensitive people.

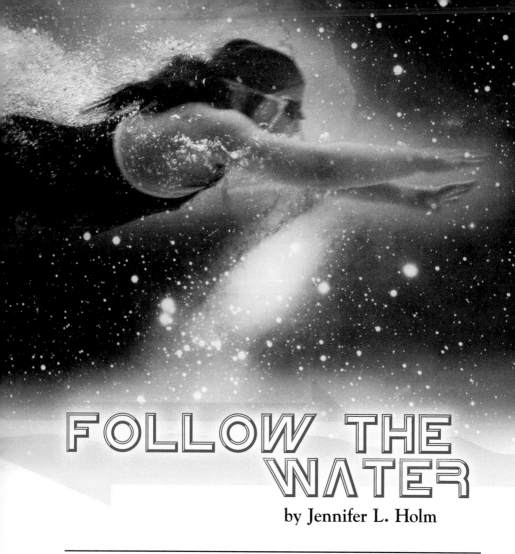

# FOLLOW THE WATER

## by Jennifer L. Holm

A teen on Mars has a tough decision to make—is she willing to risk everything to do what she wants?

I'm floating in water.

Next to me, Nana is bobbing on her back, looking up at the same blue sky, her white hair tied in a thick braid. She is wearing her lifeguard-red bathing suit, and her arms trail in the water at her sides in smooth, unhurried motions. Seagulls scream above our heads, swooping low, diving across the waves as if trying to get our attention, but it doesn't bother us. It is so peaceful out here, so perfect.

We are just two mermaids enjoying the freedom of the waves, the tug of the undertow, the rush of water all around us, part of the ocean itself.

"Georgie," Nana says, her voice smiling with pleasure. "It's heaven to be here with you."

And then a wave comes up from behind, crashes over us, and I wake up, breathing in stale musty air.

And realize I'm still on Mars.

• • • • • • • • • • • • • • • • • • • • • • • • • • • •

"Ouch!" I say.

The doctor pats my arm. "Hmm, sorry about that. I'm having a hard time finding a vein."

"Can we do this another day?" I plead. "Look at my arm!" It is covered with bruises.

"Georgiana," my mother says, shaking her head. "Come on, don't be silly."

Easy for her to say. She's not the one who's getting stuck with a needle.

"It's very important for us to gather biological <u>data</u> for future <u>colonists</u>," she adds as if this will somehow make this fun.

See, my mother's a scientist. Actually, she's a <u>geologist</u> like my father and they live for experiments and collecting data. My parents love Mars, which kind of makes sense, I guess, since Mars is really just a big rock. They spend hours talking about geological formations and whether the Holden Crater was once a lake. But when it comes to anything involving people or feelings she doesn't have a clue. ❶

> ❶ **Making Inferences**
> How does Georgie seem to feel about her mother?

---

## Vo•cab•u•lary

**data** (DAY tuh) information
**colonists** (KOL uh nists) people who live in a newly settled area
**geologist** (jee OL uh jist) a person who studies the soil and rocks

"I'm sick of this," I say, <u>reluctantly</u> baring my arm for the doctor. "I feel like a lab rat."

The doctor shrugs at me <u>apologetically</u>. "We have to keep an eye on you. We still don't know how the lower gravity will affect your development."

I've heard this about a million times. I'm not even supposed to be here. Only adults over eighteen are allowed to go to Mars but they let me come because they thought I'd finished puberty. Mars gravity is one-third of Earth's and I guess they want to avoid turning us into <u>mutants</u>. Although I suppose I could tell them a thing or two about their mutant theory of gravity. See, I've grown four inches in the time I've been here. Not that I'm complaining. I was kind of on the short side before anyway.

We are the fourth wave of pioneers, known as Fourths. The second wave <u>erected</u> the medical cabin I am standing in. It's thick black plastic, sturdy enough to protect us from the <u>solar UV</u> <u>radiation</u>, which could kill you, give you terrible skin cancer. That's what the Firsts found out. Some of them came back and had to have their noses removed. Pretty gross, if you ask me. Now the whole compound is a rabbit's warren of connecting plastic tunnels.

I guess there's nothing like a little death and disaster to make you figure out how to do things right. But all those unmanned robots that explored the planet seemed pretty good. They <u>transmitted</u> back maps, and geological findings, and climate

---

## Vo•cab•u•lary

**reluctantly** (rih LUK tunt lee) unwillingly
**apologetically** (uh pol uh JET ik lee) in a way that suggests being sorry
**mutants** (MYOOT unts) living things with new characteristics that result from altered genes
**erected** (ih REK ted) built
**solar** (SOH lur) of the sun
**UV** (yoo vee) abbreviation for ultraviolet, a type of light that can damage skin
**radiation** (ray dee AY shun) particles sent out by a radioactive source, such as the sun's rays
**transmitted** (trans MIT tid) sent

information. So that by the time the first fifty people and one dog were sent to Mars, they thought they knew the score.

But, I mean, I suppose it's not easy to organize the pesky little business of living on a deserted rock in the middle of space. There's the crazy weather, and the subzero freezing cold, and the dust storms, and the little fact that it takes six months to get here packed on a shuttle like a bunch of sardines. In my opinion, there's a pretty good reason that Mars is <u>uninhabited</u>, but why would anyone listen to a fourteen-year-old? ❷

❷ **Questioning**
What are some of the challanges of living on Mars?

The doctor jabs the needle in my arm again. It stings and I <u>wince</u>.

"There we go," he says. "Just relax."

I watch as a tube of dark red blood is sucked out. The doctor yanks the needle out, slaps on a Band-Aid, and as I rub my arm, I can't help but wonder if they sent this guy to Mars to get him off Earth. Talk about bedside manner.

"There. That wasn't so bad, now was it?" my mother says brightly.

"Whoops," the doctor says. "I need one more tube."

"No more blood," I say.

I put up with a lot on this planet.

___

## Vo•cab•u•lary

**uninhabited** (un in HAB ih tid) having no people
**wince** (wintz) to make a startled movement; to flinch

Like no friends, and <u>rehydrated</u> food, and having to perform like a pony on transmissions for kids back home, but enough is enough.

"Georgiana," my mother says, looking at the doctor.

"No more!" I run to the door, and then freeze. Because on this dumb planet I can't even make a dramatic exit.

I have to put on my stupid survival suit first.

I flip open the flap and head down the plastic hallway. It's eerily quiet, the way it always gets before a bad dust storm hits, and I shiver a little.

It's cold on Mars, colder than you can even imagine. The average temperature is negative eighty-one degrees, and believe me, that's pretty darn cold when you have to go to the bathroom in the middle of the night.

On the trip here, I read a book called *Red Mars,* by this guy Kim Stanley Robinson. It's this famous science fiction book written a long time ago about what Mars might be like for the first colonists. In it, the Mars colonists live a pretty comfortable life in these beautiful domed cities that have amazing views of the surrounding landscape. He made it sound not half bad, actually. And then I got here.

Which is why I guess it's called science fiction and not reality. ❸

> **❸ Analyzing**
> How does real life on Mars differ from the way it's described in *Red Mars*?

But Mr. Robinson did get the part about the dust right. See, the dust on Mars is so superfine, so microscopic, that it blows right through all the plastic tents we live in. The plastic keeps the air in and the UV rays out, but not the dust. I don't know why. And it's everywhere. In your eyes, in your ears, in your hair. Even your belly button. Most of the people who live here seem to get used to it, but not me. I mean, how do you get used to finding dust up

### Vo•cab•u•lary

**rehydrated** (ree HY dray tid) restored to its original form by adding water

your nose every morning? Not to mention, it's impossible to get the taste out of your mouth, rusty, like you're losing a tooth.

I take the tunnel that leads to the <u>Sojourner</u>. Since there's nowhere to go and nothing to do here, everyone can usually be found there after dinner. It's not like they have much of a choice. It's the only bar on Mars.

The place is packed, and when I open the door, a blast of warm air hits me.

The bar itself is a long piece of one of the early shuttles that came to Mars. It only made one trip, and then it blew an engine. It was a lousy shuttle, but it's a pretty cool bar.

Sammy the bartender is polishing the surface with a wet cloth when I grab a stool. He nods when he sees me. "Hey, Georgiana. How's it going?"

My real name is Georgiana, but I prefer Georgie. Not that it matters. I've learned that people pretty much call you what they want.

"Okay."

"The usual?"

The usual is a cherry cola, but I have other ideas tonight. After all, in a few short hours I will be fifteen.

"Uh no," I say, looking around. I put my elbows on the bar and try to look casual, like I've done this before. "I was thinking maybe a beer."

"A beer?" Sammy asks, raising a <u>skeptical</u> eyebrow.

"Yes," I say, struggling to keep my voice from wavering. "A beer."

He shakes his head at me, a stern expression on his face. "You know I can't serve you. You're too young, Georgiana."

---

### Vo•cab•u•lary

**Sojourner** (SOH jurn er) the bar is named after the first robotic vehicle used on Mars
**skeptical** (SKEP tuh kul) doubtful

"It's not like I'm gonna get drunk and get in a driving accident or anything," I say, exasperated.

The guy next to me, Merrick, says, "You trying to buy a beer, Georgiana?"

"No," I whisper fiercely, looking down.

Merrick's a cellular biologist, and has like ten Ph.D.'s so you'd think he'd be a little <u>perceptive</u>, right? Instead, he turns to the room and announces loudly, "Hey everyone! Our little Georgiana's trying to buy a beer."

The bar bursts into hoots of laughter and clapping and shouts. I put my hands over my face, wishing I could just disappear.

I mean, this is my life.

I can't even sneak my first beer without the entire planet knowing.

The only reason I'm even here is because my father is a geologist, and the last batch of geologists they sent up got killed in a spring dust storm, and since then the geologists aren't exactly lining up to go to Mars anymore. Also because most of the geologists who got killed had been students of my father. He's one of the only geologists in the world who knows anything about Mars because he was on the original exploratory missions.

After the Spring Disaster, as the media called it, the government begged my father to go back to Mars, which he wanted to do anyway. You could see it in his eyes every time they sent up a new batch of settlers. His one condition was that I come. **4**

You would think I'd be pretty happy to go to Mars. I mean, it's kind of like every kid's dream, right? But I can't stop thinking about water. Anything to do with water. Like going for a swim or taking a shower or even having a real bath.

> **4 Questioning**
> How did Georgie end up on Mars?

---

## Vo•cab•u•lary

**perceptive** (pur SEP tuv) aware

Because we don't have any water.

Once every two months a shuttle arrives with drinking water, but that's only a <u>supplement</u>. See, our main source of water is from recycling. You got it. We recycle everything—the water you spit out when you brush your teeth, the leftover water from washing dishes, even when you pee—it all gets filtered and put back into the system, and everybody gets a daily ration. It tastes awful, and there's never enough to do anything more than take a sponge bath. Trust me, there's a good reason we're always wearing hats in the television broadcasts.

That's why my father's here in the first place. To find water. The geologists who died in the Spring Disaster were near the south polar cap looking for water when the dust storm hit. It's not as easy as you'd think to find water. Some whiz of a scientist told

## Vo·cab·u·lary

**supplement** (SUP luh ment) something added to make up for what is missing

**57**

NASA that they should "Follow the water," that is, follow the scientific evidence of where it's been before, to find new water. Unfortunately they think this planet was once covered with an ocean, so that's a lot of territory to cover. Which is why they need the geologists.

Once they find the water, they can start fixing up the planet, and then lots of people can come. It will be a whole new world for people to mess up and overpopulate.

I mean, I know we're here for a good reason, but speaking from personal experience, who cares about saving mankind when you can't wash your hair?

My parents are waiting for me when I get back to the cabin.

I groan when I see the expression on their faces. News travels fast on a planet where there are only two hundred and three people, and I figure they've heard about my trying to buy a beer.

I start to explain. "Look," I say, "I just wanted a sip. It wasn't anything serious—"

"Georgiana," my mother says in a calm voice. Too calm. "We just got a <u>transmission</u> from Earth."

This isn't what I was expecting.

"We weren't even going to tell you, but—"

"But what?" I'm getting a bad feeling here.

My father takes off his glasses and cleans them with a corner of his shirt. He puts them back on and says wearily, "Nana's been diagnosed with stomach cancer."

"She's dying," my mother says.

Nana was the one who taught me how to swim.

All those summers my parents spent at NASA, or on the International Space Station, I'd go to the Jersey Shore and live with Nana in her sweet little yellow house looking out on the

---

## Vo•cab•u•lary

**transmission** (trans MISH un) a message sent from one place to another

beach. Truth be told, those summers were the best parts of my life. I looked forward to them all year. Part of me still wishes I could have just lived with Nana forever.

"Your parents love you," she always says, and I know they do, but it's like they weren't the right kind of people to have kids. You can just see that they forget I'm here sometimes, like an experiment that's slipped their minds. Especially my dad. We look nothing alike, and I swear there are days when I wonder if I'm someone else's baby they picked up in the hospital by mistake. I mean, I'm almost fifteen and he still hasn't figured out that I hate to be called Georgiana.

But Nana knows everything about me. My dreams, my goals, my fears. Stuff that I could never tell my parents. Like how I wanted to get a place on the swim team (I did), and that I was worried my folks would pressure me to become a scientist like them (they did), and how I wished a cute boy named Chen would kiss me (he did, behind the gym at school—it was very nice).

The truth is, she's the thing I miss the most from Earth. Sure, I hate the dust, and not being able to take a bath or have a conversation with someone my own age, but there are days when I think I'll go crazy from the loneliness of not being able to talk to her. ❺ And every time I dream about water, I dream of Nana and me together.

The two mermaids in the middle of the ocean.

> ❺ **Analyzing**
> Why is Georgie's relationship with Nana so important to her?

I just know she'd laugh at the way we live in plastic tents. "Why, you all look like hamsters," she'd say, and she'd be right. She's just that kind of person. She tells it like it is.

She's the only person in the whole world who's ever believed in me.

And they weren't going to tell me?

"So when are we going back?" I say.

"We're not," my mom says.

"What are you talking about? We can't just leave Nana alone." Nana is my father's mother, and he's an only child. We're all she has.

"Honey," my mom says. "We talked to the doctors. The cancer's already spread to her <u>lymph nodes.</u> She's only got five months to live. We'd never make it back in time. She'd die before we get there."

"You don't know that for sure! You're just guessing," I say.

My dad, ever the compassionate, says, "Statistically speaking, there's only a five percent chance that Nana would survive more than five months, especially given her complications."

I mean, this is how they talk.

"Well I don't care. I'm going."

"You can't go," my mom says. "Your last calcium test came back and"—and here she takes a deep breath—"and it seems that you've lost over thirty percent of your bone density."

"So what? I'll drink a lot of milk, okay?" Actually, I hate milk, especially the powdered kind we have on Mars, but I'll do anything to get back to Nana.

"You don't understand, Georgiana," my father says. "You've lost thirty percent

---

## Vo•cab•u•lary

**lymph nodes** (limf nohds) glands that help to carry fluid to the body and filter bacteria

of your bone mass. No one knows what effect that will have when you get back to Earth. Your legs could shatter from the gravity, and you may never walk again."

"You could be in a wheelchair for the rest of your life," my mother adds helpfully.

"But," I say, my voice wavering, "didn't you know about this before you brought me up here?"

My parents cast a sidelong glance at each other, and it is clear that neither one of these brilliant scientists thought this one through.

"So how am I ever gonna leave Mars?" I whisper.

My dad, Mr. Mars himself, just looks at me and says quizzically, "Why would you want to leave?" **6**

Like Nana always said, just because you have brains, it doesn't mean you have sense.

> **6 Predicting**
> Will Georgie ever leave Mars?

I'm sitting at a table in the mess hall eating breakfast and generally trying to avoid everyone. It's gotten around that I tried to buy a beer last night, and I'm getting a lot of <u>condescending</u> warnings about the <u>perils</u> of alcohol. I want to say that I think a sip of beer is hardly the most life-threatening thing considering I just found out all my bones are going to melt if I ever go back to Earth.

"Hey, brat."

I look up and see Buddy standing there holding a tray.

Buddy is twenty-one, and a marine. Everyone here is either a scientist or in the military. Some paranoid politician back in Washington seems to think that another country might get it into their heads to send a shuttle up here to claim a chunk of Mars to use as a military outpost. In my opinion, anyone who actually *wants* to come to a planet where you can't take a bath is too

---

### Vo•cab•u•lary

**condescending** (kon duh SEN ding) in a way that puts someone down
**perils** (PAIR ulz) dangers

stupid to be much of a national security threat.

Buddy's hair is cut short in a buzz, and the skin on his face is dry and flaky, which isn't any surprise because mine is the same way. When there's no water on a planet, it's hard to keep your skin moist and glowing. Still, I like Buddy. He's funny, and even though he's a marine, he's one of the few adults who doesn't talk to me like I'm a little kid or an idiot.

He sits down, starts digging into his rehydrated eggs. "Dust storm's coming," he says.

What else is new.

I pick up a toffee candy that they leave out in bowls on the tables at every meal. People eat them like crazy. I mean, if there was no toffee, there'd be like a rebellion or a <u>mutiny</u> or something.

"How's it going?" he asks, pausing to look up.

"I've had better days," I say.

Buddy squints across at me. "Heard about last night."

I don't say anything.

"I wouldn't worry about it. People like to talk," he says in a <u>consoling</u> voice. "By the way, happy birthday."

"I don't care about last night," I say.

"Oh?"

"My grandmother has cancer. She's gonna die. In five months."

He blinks. "Whoa. That's terrible."

I shake my head. "She's always been so healthy. She was an Olympic swimmer."

---

### Vo·cab·u·lary

**mutiny** (MYOO tuh nee) a revolt
**consoling** (kun SOHL ing) soothing

"No kidding."

I nod. "She won a gold medal. Backstroke." And then it all comes out in a painful rush. "My parents refuse to go back to Earth to see her. They say she's going to die before they get there, and they won't let me go because apparently I've lost thirty percent of my bones and they think my body will shatter or something."

He puts down his fork, sits back. "Talk about a lousy birthday present."

"No kidding."

"Why did they even bring you?"

Good question.

"Maybe you should leave now, you know, before it gets any worse. Have you talked to the doc about it yet?"

"No," I say. "It doesn't matter, though. My parents won't let me go."

"You can always stow away," he says jokingly. "That's what my grandfather did."

"What do you mean?"

"My grandfather grew up on a farm, and he hated it, so he ran away and stowed aboard a navy ship. Ended up in Hawaii." His beeper goes off, and he looks down. "Gotta go, brat. Ask the doc."

I stare at him. I don't exactly have a lot of faith in adults these days. Especially the ones who suck my blood out.

"Ask the doc," Buddy says again. **7** He stands up, pockets a handful of toffees and winks at me. "I just love this candy. Takes the taste of dust away."

He buckles into his suit and disappears out the door.

Even though I live on a planet with some of the smartest

> **7 Questioning**
> Why does Buddy tell Georgie to talk to the doctor?

scientists in the world, I swear it's the most intelligent conversation I've had in months.

• • • • • • • • • • • • • • • • • • • • • • • • • • • •

"Nobody really knows what will happen to you. You're the first adolescent to live on Mars, Georgiana," the doctor says, as he looks at me from behind his big desk.

Like I don't know this already? Trust me, I am very well aware that there's not a boy within sixty-seven million miles who can kiss me.

"What's the worst-case scenario?" I ask.

His gaze doesn't waver. "Your leg bones will shatter from the force of Earth's gravity and you'll never walk again."

I let that sink in. "Okay, what else could happen?"

He leans back in his chair, folds his hands. "Your legs would sustain massive fractures and you'd spend months in a full body cast. In the best-case scenario, you wouldn't sustain any breaks and would require hospitalization to build up your calcium." **8**

"How long would that be?"

He purses his lips, considering. "A minimum of four to five months, I imagine, on a full <u>regimen</u> of IV-delivered drugs. It will take at least that long to build up some of the lost calcium. And even after that you'll have to be very careful and restrict your activity. Physical therapy, too, I imagine." He shrugs. "It's really hard to say."

> **8 Questioning**
> What possible risks will Georgie face if she returns to Earth?

Is he serious? Four to five months in a hospital with a needle in my arm? I hate needles, I really do, especially after spending the last year being poked and prodded and measured.

"What would you do if you were me?" I ask the doctor.

"Ah," he says. "But I'm not you."

---

### Vo•cab•u•lary

**regimen** (REJ uh mun) a schedule

And that's when I realize I'm in this alone.

"Sweetie," my mom says a few days later as I lay in my bunk. "We know you're feeling a bit down about Nana, so your dad has a little birthday surprise for you. Don't you, honey?"

"Well," he says excitedly. "I got permission for us to take a rover out!"

I roll my eyes. Just what I need. Another rock-hunting expedition.

"I'm really not up to looking at rocks," I say.

"But we're not going to look at rocks," he says. "It's even better."

This should be good. My dad's idea of a fun time is taking core samples.

"Come on," my mother says, tugging me up. "I promise you'll like it."

## Vo•cab•u•lary

**rover** (ROH vur) a robotic vehicle

My dad drives the rover out. We are wearing our survival suits, breathing an air mixture.

He parks the rover, gets out, and starts walking away from us, but I just stare. We are all alone in the middle of Mars and it's strange how <u>serene</u> it is—the horizon unbroken by buildings or trees or anything but a rolling rock-studded surface, an alien desert.

"This way," my dad calls over his mike. "Race you to the edge!"

And then we are bounding across the landscape and I'm leaping over big boulders with an ease I could never have done on Earth and it's such a rush, this feeling coursing through me, my heart pounding, my lungs inflating, as if every cell in me is shouting—so healthy! so alive!—that it seems <u>inconceivable</u> that this same strong body may not support me on Earth.

I stop suddenly, my dad a step ahead, my breath caught in my throat. We are standing on the edge of a huge canyon, winding and wild, something out of a movie. It is the most beautiful thing I have ever seen, I think. It's awesome in its rawness, like the ocean, and a strange peace steals over me.

"That," my dad says, "is the Nirgal Vallis. We think there was once a big river there."

"Like the Grand Canyon?" I say.

"Exactly, Georgiana," my mom says.

"And see right there? That red flag?" my dad says, pointing to a stretch of cliff where a little red flag waves merrily.

"Uh-huh."

He clears his throat importantly. "That little spot is where I found a downward smear of water-soluble mineral deposits in a core sample." He draws the moment out. "I figure we drill about four hundred meters down and we'll hit water," he says with a wink.

---

## Vo•cab•u•lary

**serene** (suh REEN) peaceful
**inconceivable** (in kun SEE vuh bul) unbelievable

"Really?" Even I can't keep the excitement out of my voice. *They found water!*

"Really," my mom says, smiling at my dad proudly. "Your dad's a smart guy." She grasps his hand.

"Does anybody know yet?" I ask.

"Not yet. We won't announce it until we know for sure," my dad says.

"But we will," my mom adds confidently.

"The signs are all there," he says.

I stare at my dad. "But how do you know you'll find water, Dad? I mean, how can you know for sure?"

And then he says something that shocks me.

"Nothing's ever certain, Georgiana," my dad, the scientist, says. His voice crackles over the mike. "You just have to have hope." **9**

**9 Making Inferences**
Why is Georgie shocked by what her father says?

I'm bobbing in the ocean, my wet hair plastering my face, the scent of salt in the air. The water's warm, and I turn and there is Nana right beside me.

"Nana," I cry, hugging her tight, embracing her sturdy body, comforting like Christmas. "I've missed you so."

"Why, I've missed you, too, Georgie," she says, pushing a strand of hair out of my face.

"You don't look like you're dying," I say.

"Who said I was dying? I'm healthy as a horse!"

And she looks it. Her cheeks are ruddy, her skin is flush with good health, even her eyes are shining.

"I want to do something," I say. "But I'm a little scared."

"You can do whatever you want to do," she says. "You always could."

"I want to come home," I say simply. "And be with you."

"But, Georgie," she says, her eyes twinkling, "you're already home."

And then I wake up alone in the dark little plastic cabin and hear the dust storm raging outside and I can't help myself.

I just cry.

Buddy sidles up to me in the mess hall with a full tray of food. People are <u>lingering</u> over their precious cups of coffee and chewing on toffees.

"You been crying, brat?"

I glare at him.

"So did you see the doc?" he presses.

"Yeah. Great news. Best-case scenario I have to be in a hospital for four or five months hooked up to an IV. Worst case, I'm crippled for life." I swallow hard. "And Nana's all alone," I whisper, my voice breaking.

He clears his throat. "My grandfather died from cancer too. They gave him three months to live. And you know how long he lasted?"

"How long?" I whisper, hope lodged in my throat.

"A whole year."

I'd settle for a week with Nana, I think.

His beeper goes off and he groans. "There goes dinner. Shuttle just got in."

"Shuttle?"

"Supply shuttle. I'm helping to unload it. It's on a quick turnaround. Just dropping off supplies and then heading back to Earth in the morning." He stands abruptly.

The dust storm is roaring outside, but the only thing I hear is that one little word.

Earth.

---

## Vo•cab•u•lary

**lingering** (LING gur ing) waiting around

I grab his wrist. "Maybe I could bring you some coffee in the morning. You know, over at the shuttle," I say casually, looking him straight in the eye, willing him to hear me.

Buddy unwraps a toffee, sticks it in his mouth, chews for a moment, and stares at me. There's a curious expression on his face.

"Sure," he says finally. "How about at oh-seven-hundred?"

Over his shoulder, I see my parents enter the cafeteria, holding hands and laughing, and something inside me goes still. Suddenly, all these little things seem so important—this candy, those smiles, these two strong legs. How can I possibly give this up?

Buddy sees where I'm looking and shakes his head.

"You sure you know what you're doing? Have you thought about it? You know, your legs?" he asks.

"Nothing's certain," I say, and know that I am my father's daughter after all. "But you just have to have hope." **10**

**10 Predicting**
What does Georgie plan to do?

The next morning when I wake up my parents are getting ready to head out.

"Your dad and I are going out with the Alpha team to Nirgal Vallis. We won't be back until late tonight," my mom says excitedly.

She is wearing her exploration suit, and she looks so happy, like she's about to burst.

"This is it, Georgie," she whispers, her face one big grin. "I know we're going to find water today. You'll have your very own pool in no time at all!"

"I know you will too," I say, and can't help but think how ironic it is that I'm leaving this planet just when it's getting good.

Still, I hug her hard. "I love you, Mom."

---

## Vo•cab•u•lary

**ironic** (eye RAW nik) not what was expected

My dad's almost out the door when I stop him, hug him hard too. He's startled.

"Good luck," I say.

And then they are gone.

• • • • • • • • • • • • • • • • • • • • • • • • •

Buddy is waiting for me when I bring over the thermos of coffee. It's the beginning of the shift and he's the only one there.

"Hey, brat," he says.

"Hey, Buddy," I blush, holding my duffel.

"The closet in the back is cleared out for you. Door's open. There's a blanket and some other stuff there too."

"Here," I say, and give him my dog-eared copy of *Red Mars* by Kim Stanley Robinson.

He raises a curious eyebrow.

"It's this science fiction book," I say, "about the first colonists on Mars."

Buddy laughs at me. "Does he get it right?"

I grin back. "Sort of. Although I kind of like his version better."

Buddy nods.

I hesitate for a moment, stare down at my legs. Can I really do this? I mean, talk about deserving a sip of beer.

He pats my cheek, and says, "Don't worry. You'll be fine. Just have them hook you up in the same hospital your grandmother's in. That way you can be together. It won't be so bad."

"Thanks," I whisper.

"You better get moving, brat. The captain's just about finishing breakfast now." He gives me a goofy little grin. "And hey, take a swim for me, okay?"

"Only if you take one for me," I say, and he shoots me a quizzical look.

"What?" he asks, but I just smile mysteriously at him. He'll know what I mean soon enough.

After all, news travels fast on this planet.

• • • • • • • • • • • • • • • • • • • • • • • • • • • •

As the engines roar to life I settle back and close my eyes, imagining Mars disappearing behind me, and all that blue water ahead. A whole world of it. And there, in the middle of it all, is Nana with her warm smile and steady eyes.

I can almost hear her voice. "Georgie," she will say. "It's heaven to be here with you."

They should be finding my note right about now, I figure. **11** ○

**11 Analyzing**
What lesson about life do you learn from this story?

---

**Answering the**
**BIG Question**

**As you do the following activities, consider the Big Question:**
**How do you stay true to yourself?**

**WRITE TO LEARN** What will happen to Georgie after she returns to Earth? In your Learner's Notebook, write a brief entry describing what you think will happen after her long voyage.

**LITERATURE GROUPS** Meet with two or three others who have read "Follow the Water." Discuss Georgie's decision to return to Earth. Do you agree with that decision? Why or why not?

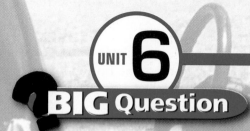

# How do you keep from giving up when bad things happen?

Bad things happen—from flunking a test to losing someone you love. As you read the following selections, you'll discover a variety of ways in which to think about the question: **How do you keep from giving up when bad things happen?** Some of the situations and characters may help you come up with your own answer to that question.

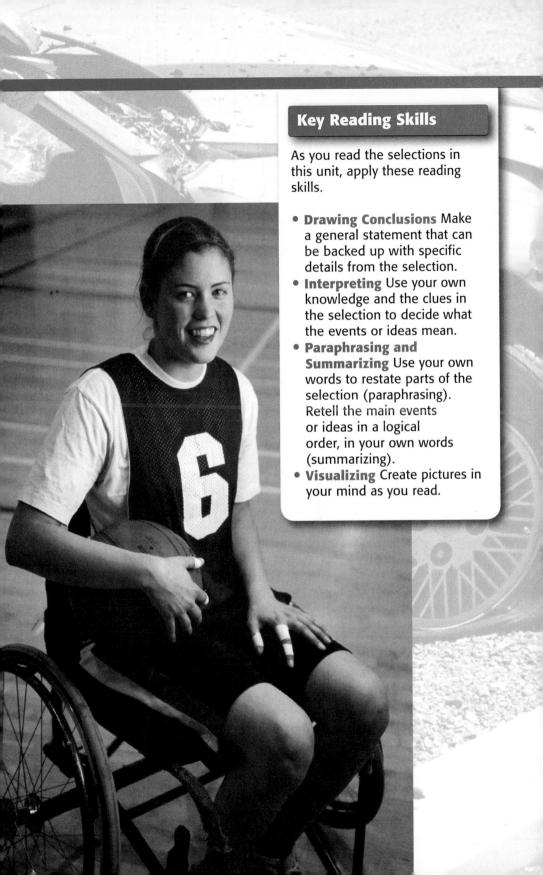

## Key Reading Skills

As you read the selections in this unit, apply these reading skills.

- **Drawing Conclusions** Make a general statement that can be backed up with specific details from the selection.
- **Interpreting** Use your own knowledge and the clues in the selection to decide what the events or ideas mean.
- **Paraphrasing and Summarizing** Use your own words to restate parts of the selection (paraphrasing). Retell the main events or ideas in a logical order, in your own words (summarizing).
- **Visualizing** Create pictures in your mind as you read.

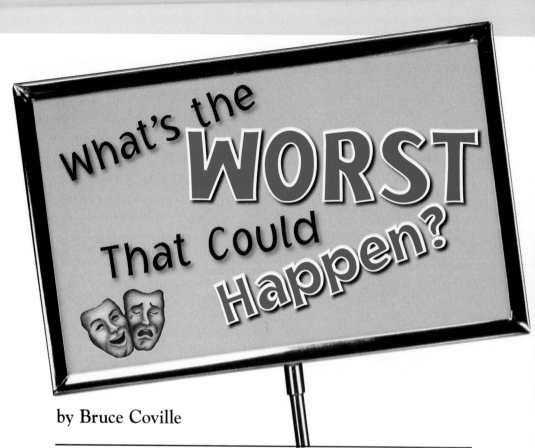

# What's the WORST That Could Happen?

## by Bruce Coville

**A big-time crush and a case of stage fright are a recipe for disaster on the night of a school performance.**

If thirteen is supposed to be an unlucky number, what does it mean that we are forced to go through an entire year with that as our age? I mean, you would think a <u>civilized</u> society would just come up with a way for us to skip it.

Of course, good luck and I have rarely shared the same park bench. Sometimes I think Murphy's Law—you know, "If something can go wrong, it will"—was invented just for me. I suppose the fact that my name is Murphy Murphy might have something to do with that feeling.

---

**Vo·cab·u·lary**

**civilized** (SIV ul yzd) highly developed

Yeah, you read it right: Murphy Murphy. It's like a family curse. The last name I got from my father, of course. The first name came down from my mother's side, where it is a tradition for the firstborn son. You would think my mother might have considered that before she married Dad, but love makes fools of us all, I guess. Anyway, the fact that I got stuck with the same name coming and going, so to speak, shows that my parents are either spineless (my theory) or have no common sense (my sister's theory).

I would like to note that no one has ever apologized to me for this name. "I think it's lovely," says my mother—which, when you consider it, would seem to support my sister's theory. Anyway, you can see that right from the beginning of my life, if something could go wrong, it did.

Okay, I suppose it could have been worse. I could have been born dead or with two heads or something. On the other hand, as I lie here in my hospital bed trying to work out exactly how I got here, there are times when I wonder if being born dead might not have been the best thing. **1**

**1 Drawing Conclusions**
Do you think Murphy is serious when he says this? Explain.

To begin with, I want to say here and now that Mikey Farnsworth should take at least part of the blame for this situation. This, by the way, is true for many of the bad things that have happened in my life, from the paste-eating incident in first grade through the <u>bogus</u> fire-drill situation last year, right up to yesterday afternoon, which was sort of the Olympics of Bad Luck as far as I'm concerned. What's amazing is that somehow Mikey ends up coming out of these things looking perfectly fine. He is, as my grandfather likes to say, the kind of guy who can fall in a manure pile and come out smelling like a rose.

The one I am not going to blame is Tiffany Grimsley, though if I hadn't had this stupid crush on her, it never would have happened.

---

## Vo•cab•u•lary
**bogus** (BOH gis) fake

# What's the Worst That Could Happen?

Okay, I want to stop and talk about this whole thing of having a crush. Let me say right up front that it is very confusing and not something I am used to. When it started, I was totally baffled. I mean, I don't even like girls, and all of a sudden I keep thinking about one of them? Give me a break!

In case it hasn't happened to you yet, let me warn you. Based on personal experience, I can say that while there are many bad things about having a crush, just about the worst of them is the stupid things you will do because of it.

Okay, let's back up here.

I probably wouldn't even have known I had a crush to begin with if Mikey hadn't informed me of this fact. "Man, you've got it bad for Tiffany," he says one day when we are poking around in the swamp behind his house.

"What are you talking about?" I ask. At the same time, my cheeks begin to burn as if they are on fire. Startled, I lift my foot to tie my shoe, which is a trick I learned in an exercise magazine and that has become sort of a habit. At the moment, it is mostly an excuse to look down.

What the heck is going on here? I think.

Mikey laughs. "Look at you blush, Murphy! There's no point in trying to hide it. I watched you drooling over her in social studies class today. And you've only mentioned her, like, sixteen times since we got home this afternoon."

"Well, sure, but that's because she's a friend," I say, desperately trying to avoid the horrible truth. "We've known each other since kindergarten, for Pete's sake."

Mikey laughs again, and I can tell I'm not fooling him. "What am I going to do?" I groan.

He shrugs. "Either you suffer in silence, or you tell her you like her."

Is he nuts? If you tell a girl you like her, it puts you totally out in the open. I mean, you've got no place to hide. And there are really only two possible responses you're going to get from her: (a) She likes you, too, which the more you think about it, the more unlikely it seems; or (b) anything else, which is, like, totally, utterly humiliating. I'm sure girls have problems of their own. But I don't think they have any idea of the sheer terror a guy has to go through before any boy-girl stuff can get started.

I sure hope this gets easier with time, because I personally really don't understand how the human race has managed to survive this long, given how horrifying it is to think about telling a girl you like her.

Despite Mikey's accusation, I do not think I have actually drooled over Tiffany during social studies class. But it is hard not to think about her then, because she sits right in front of me. It's the last class of the day, and the October sunlight comes in slantwise and catches in her golden hair in a way that makes it hard to breathe. ❷

❷ **Visualizing**
Picture the classroom scene that Murphy describes here.

It does not help that eighth-grade social studies is taught by Herman Fessenden, who you will probably see on the front of the *National Enquirer* someday as a mass murderer for boring twenty-six kids to death in a single afternoon. It hasn't happened yet, but I'm sure it's just a matter of time.

I spend the entire weekend thinking about what Mikey has said, and I come up with a bold plan, which is to pass Tiffany a note asking if she wants to grab a slice of pizza at Angelo's after school. I am just getting up my nerve to do it—there are only five minutes of class left—when Mr. F. says, "So, what do you think the queen should have done then, Murphy?"

How am I supposed to know? But I blush and don't hand the note to Tiffany after all, which wouldn't have been so bad, except that Butch Coulter saw I had it and grabs it on the way

out of class, and I have to give him the rest of my week's lunch money to get it back.

Tuesday I try a new tactic. There's a little store on the way to school where you can pick up candy and gum and stuff, and I get some on the way to school and then kind of poke Tiff in the back during social studies class, which is about the only time I see her, to ask if she wants a piece of gum. Only before she can answer, Mr. Fessenden comes up from behind and snatches the whole pack out of my hand. So that was that.

Then, on Wednesday, it's as if the gods are smiling on me, which is not something I am used to. Tiffany grabs my arm on the way out of social studies and says, "Can I talk to you for a second, Murphy?"

"Sure," I say. This is not very <u>eloquent</u>, but it is better than the first thought that crosses my mind, which is, "Anytime, anywhere, any moment of the day." It is also better than, "Your words would be like nectar flowing into the hungry mouths of my ears," which was a line I had come up with for a poem I was writing about her.

She actually looks a little shy, though what this goddess-on-Earth has to be shy about is more than I can imagine.

She hands me a folded-up set of papers, and my heart skips a beat. Can this be a love letter? If so, it's a really long one.

"I wrote this skit for drama club, and I thought maybe you would do it with me next Friday. I think you'd be just right for the part."

My heart starts pounding. While it seems unlikely that the part is that of a barbarian warrior prince, just doing it means I will

---

## Vo•cab•u•lary

**eloquent** (EL uh kwint) smoothly spoken

have an excuse to spend time with Tiffany. I mean, we'll have to rehearse and . . . well, the imagination staggers.

"Yes!" I say, ignoring the facts that (a) I have not yet read the script and (b) I have paralyzing stage fright.

She gives me one of those sunrise smiles of hers, grabs my arm and gives it a squeeze, and says, "Thanks. This is going to be fun." Then she's gone, leaving me with a memory of her fingers on my arm and a wish that I had started pumping iron when I was in first grade, so my biceps would have been ready for this moment. **3**

Mikey moves in a second later. "Whoa," he says, nudging me with his elbow. "Progress! What did she say?"

"She wants me to do a skit with her."

He shakes his head. "Too bad. I thought maybe you had a chance. How'd she take it when you told her no?"

**3 Summarizing**
In a sentence or two, tell what happens after social studies class on Wednesday.

I look at him in surprise. "I didn't. I said I would do it."

Mikey looks even more surprised. "Murphy, you can't go onstage with her. You can't even move when you get onstage. Don't you remember what happened in fifth grade?"

As if I could forget. Not only was it one of the three most humiliating moments of my life, but according to my little brother, it has become legendary at Westcott Elementary. Here's the short version: Mrs. Carmichael had cast me as George Washington in our class play, and I was, I want to tell you, pretty good during rehearsals. But when they opened the curtain and I saw the audience . . . well, let's just say that when my mother saw the look on my face, she actually let out a scream. She told me later she thought I was having a heart attack. As for me, my mouth went drier than day-old toast, some mysterious object wedged itself in my throat, and the only reason I didn't bolt from the stage was that I couldn't move my arms or legs. Heck, I couldn't even move my fingers.

I couldn't even squeak!

Finally, they had to cancel the performance. Even after the curtains were closed, it took two teachers and a janitor to carry me back to the classroom.

"This time will be different," I say.

Mikey snorts.

I know he is right. "Oh, man, what am I gonna do?" I wail.

"Come on, let's look at the script. Maybe all you have to do is sit there and she'll do all the acting."

No such luck. The script, which is called "Debbie and the Doofus," is very funny.

It also calls for me to say a lot of lines.

It also calls for me to act like a complete dork.

Immediately, I begin to wonder why Tiffany thinks I would be just right for this role.

"Maybe she imagines you're a brilliant actor," says Mikey.

He is trying to be helpful, but to tell the truth, I am not sure which idea is worse: that Tiffany thinks I am a dork or that she thinks I am a brilliant actor.

"What am I gonna do?" I wail again.

"Maybe your parents will move before next week," says Mikey, shaking his head. "Otherwise, you're a dead man walking." ❹

**❹ Interpreting**
What does Mikey mean when he says this?

I ask, but my parents are not planning on moving.

I study the script as if it is the final exam for life, which as far as I am concerned, it is. After two days I know not only my lines, but all of Tiffany's lines, too, as well as the lines for Laurel Gibbon, who is going to be playing the waitress at a little restaurant where we go for our bad date.

My new theory is that I will enjoy rehearsals and the excuse they give me to be with Tiffany, and then pray for a meteor to strike me before the day of the performance.

The first half of the theory actually seems to work. We have two rehearsals—one at school and one in Tiffany's rec room. At the first one she is very impressed by the fact that I know my lines already. "This is great, Murphy!" she says, which makes me feel as if I have won the lottery.

At the second rehearsal I actually make Laurel, who is perhaps the most solemn girl in school, laugh. This is an amazing sound to me, and I find that I really enjoy it. Like Tiffany, Laurel has been in our class since kindergarten. Only I never noticed her much because, well, no one ever notices Laurel much, on account of she basically doesn't talk. I wondered at first why Tiffany had cast her, but it turns out they are in the same church group and have been good friends for a long time.

Sometimes I think the girls in our class have a whole secret life that I don't know about.

Time becomes very weird. Sometimes it seems as if the hours are rushing by in a blur, the moment of performance hurtling toward me. Other times the clock seems to poke along like a sloth with <u>chronic fatigue syndrome</u>. Social studies class consists of almost nothing but staring at the sunshine in Tiffany's hair and flubbing the occasional question that Mr. Fessenden lobs at me. Some days I think he asks me questions out of pure meanness. Other days he leaves me alone, and I almost get the impression he feels sorry for me.

Mikey and I talk about the situation every night. "No meteor yet," he'll say, shaking his head.

---

## Vo•cab•u•lary

**chronic fatigue syndrome** (KRON ik  fuh TEEG  SIN drum) an illness that has profound tiredness as its main symptom

"What am I gonna do?" I reply, repeating the question that haunts my days. I can't possibly tell Tiffany I can't do this.

"Maybe you could be sick that day?" says Mikey.

I shake my head. "If I let her down, I will hate myself forever."

Mikey rolls his eyes. "Maybe you should run away from home," he suggests, not very helpfully.

Finally, we do come up with a plan, which is that Mikey will stay in the wings to prompt me in case the entire script falls out of my head. I don't know if this will really do much good, since if I freeze with terror, mere prompting will not be of any use. On the other hand, knowing Mikey will be there calms me down a little. It's like having a life jacket.

Ha! Little do I know what kind of life jacket he will turn out to be.

To my <u>dismay</u>, I have not been able to <u>parlay</u> my time working on the skit with Tiffany into anything bigger. ❺ This is partly because she is the busiest person in the eighth grade, with more clubs and committees and activities than any normal person could ever be involved with. It is also because I am stupid about this kind of thing and don't have the slightest clue how to do it. So I treasure my memory of the two rehearsals and, more than anything else, the sound of her laughing at some of what I have done.

> ❺ **Paraphrasing**
> Use your own words to restate this sentence.

Despite my prayers, Friday arrives. I don't suppose I really expected God to cancel it, though I would have been deeply appreciative if he had. I go through the day in a state of cold terror. The drama club meeting is after school. Members of the club have invited their friends, their families, and some teachers to come see the skits. There are going to be four skits in all. Tiffany, Laurel, and I are scheduled to go last, which gives me more time to sweat and worry.

---

## Vo•cab•u•lary

**dismay** (dis MAY) condition of being worried or upset
**parlay** (PAR lay) manuever; turn into

Mikey is backstage with us, but Tiffany does not know why. I tell her he came because he is my pal. Getting him aside, I check to make sure he has the script.

At 2:45 Mrs. Whitcomb, the drama club coach, comes back to wish us luck. She makes a little speech, which she ends with, "Okay, kids—break a leg!"

This, of course, is how people wish each other luck in the theater. According to my mother, the idea is that you're not going to get your wish anyway, so you wish for the thing you don't want and you may get the thing you do want instead.

I suddenly wonder if this is what I have been doing wrong all my life.

On the other hand, Tiffany is standing next to me, so that is one wish that is continuing to come true.

"Are you excited?" she asks.

"You have no idea," I answer, with complete honesty.

Laurel, who is standing on the other side of me, whispers, "I'm scared."

"Don't worry, you'll be fine," I reply.

I am fairly confident this is true, since I expect to make such a fool of myself that no one will notice anything else anyway. Inside me, a small voice is screaming, "What were you thinking of, you moron? You are going to humiliate yourself in front of all these people, including the girl you would cut out your heart for, who will be even more humiliated than you are because it's her skit that you are messing up! Run away! Run away!"

If I could get my hands on this small voice, I would gladly beat it to a bloody pulp.

Instead, I keep taking deep breaths and reminding myself of how funny I was during the rehearsals.

The first skit goes up. I think it's funny, but at first no one laughs. This terrifies me all over again. Then someone snickers. A moment later someone else lets out a snort. Pretty soon everyone is laughing. Clearly, it takes people a while to get warmed up when they are trying to have fun.

At first the sound of that laughter is soothing. But it takes only a few minutes for me to get terrified by it. What if they don't laugh at *our* skit? Even worse, what if they laugh for the wrong reasons? What if Tiffany is totally humiliated, and it's all my fault?

I go back to wanting to die.

The second skit goes up and dies in my place. It just lies onstage, stinking the place up like a week-old fish. It's as boring as last month's newspaper. In fact, it's almost as boring as Mr. Fessenden, which I would not have thought possible. I feel a surge of hope. We can't look worse than this. In fact, next to it we'll seem like geniuses. Too bad we can't go on right away!

Unfortunately, we have to wait for the third skit, which turns out to be brilliant, which makes me want to kill the people who are in it. Now we'll be compared to them instead of the dead fish of that second skit.

The curtain closes.

"Our turn," whispers Tiffany. "Break a leg, Murphy."

"Break a leg," I murmur back. Then, so Laurel won't feel left out, I say the same thing to her as we pick up the table that is our main prop and move it onto the stage. Tiffany is right behind us with a pair of chairs. Once they're in place, we scurry to our positions, Tiffany and me stage right, Laurel stage left.

My stomach clenches. Cold sweat starts out on my brow.

"Murphy!" hisses Tiffany. "Your shoelace!"

I glance down. I have forgotten to untie it, which is the key to one of my first funny bits. Out of habit, I lift my foot to take care of the lace. At that instant the curtain opens, which startles me so much that I lose my balance and fall over, landing onstage in full view of the audience.

There they are. The enemy. The people who are going to stare at me, judge me, whisper about me tomorrow. I am so frozen with terror I cannot move. I just lie there looking at them.

And then the laugh begins. My temperature goes in two directions, my blood turning to ice at the same time that the heat rises in my face. I have a long moment of terror—well, it feels like a long moment; according to Mikey, it was less than two seconds—while I think that this is it, I will never stand up again, never come to school again, never leave my house again. I will ask whoever finally picks me up to carry me home and put me in the attic. My parents will have to shove my meals through a slot in the door because I will never be able to face another living human being.

Love saves the day. "Murphy, are you all right?" hisses Tiffany.

For the sound of that voice, I would do anything—even get back on my feet.

And then, the second miracle. Some brilliant portion of my brain realizes that this is a comedy and I have just started us off with a big laugh. I stand at the edge of the stage to do a fake knock. In rehearsal, I only mimed it. Now, for some reason, I say loudly, "Knock-knock. Knockity-knock-knock."

To my surprise, the audience finds this funny. Another laugh. ❻

**❻ Summarizing**
What happens after Murphy lifts his foot to untie his shoelace?

Tiffany comes to the door, and we go through our opening business, which establishes that she is prim and proper and I am a total idiot, which doesn't take much acting because it is pretty much real life anyway. But something is happening. I'm not making up lines, but I am making bigger gestures, broader moves, weirder voices than I did in rehearsal. People are howling. Tiffany's eyes are dancing, and I can see that she is trying not to laugh. I am feeling like a genius.

We get to the imaginary restaurant. Laurel comes out to take our order, and I have the same effect on her.

I am starting to feel as if I'm having an out-of-body experience. Who is this funny person, making everyone laugh? How long can it go on? Can I keep it going, keep cranking up the jokes, hold on to this glorious lightning bolt I'm riding?

Laurel disappears to get our order. I fake blowing my nose on the cloth napkin, then inspecting it to see the results. I act as if I am fascinated by my imaginary boogers. Tiffany acts as if she is <u>repulsed</u>, but I can see she is hardly able to keep from bursting into laughter—especially when I hand the napkin across the table so she can examine it too. **7**

**7 Visualizing**
Picture this gross-out scene.

The audience is just about screaming. I am beginning to think that this kind of laughter is even better than the sound of Tiffany's voice.

Laurel comes back with our "order," which, because this is a skit and we are on a low budget, is a plate of Hostess cupcakes. Chocolate.

I am supposed to eat in a disgusting way. The script does not specify how. Still riding my wave of <u>improvisation</u> inspiration, I pick up a cupcake and stuff the entire thing into my mouth. Tiffany's eyes widen, and she turns her head to hide the laugh she can't hold in. Her shoulders are shaking. This is too good to be true.

I deliver my next line—which is about how beautiful she is—with bits of chocolate spewing out. It's disgusting but hilarious. Tiffany has tears streaming down her cheeks from trying to hold in her laughter.

---

## Vo•cab•u•lary

**repulsed** (rih PULSD) disgusted
**improvisation** (im prawv uh ZAY shun) something made up on the spot

Desperate to keep the riff going, I cram another entire cupcake into my mouth.

This is when disaster strikes. Suddenly, I discover that I can't breathe because there is a chocolate <u>logjam</u> in my throat. I only need a minute, I think, and I'll get this. I try to give my next line, but nothing comes out. Tiffany looks alarmed. The audience is still laughing, but the laughter is starting to die down, as if some of them realize I am in trouble.

Which is when Mikey comes barreling on stage from behind me, screaming, "He's choking! He's choking!" Then he grabs me around the waist and jabs his fists into my belly.

I've been Heimliched!

Those of you who know about the <u>Heimlich maneuver</u> will remember that basically it forces the air out of your lungs, blowing whatever is blocking your breathing out of your mouth.

Those of you who have been staging this in your mind as you read will remember who is directly across from me.

Those of you with even minimal powers of prediction will know what happens next. An unholy mix of partially chewed Hostess chocolate cupcakes spews out of my mouth and spatters all over Tiffany.

I am filled with deeper horror than any I have ever known. Wrenching my way out of Mikey's grasp, I bolt around the table to clean her off.

---

## Vo•cab•u•lary

**logjam** (LOG jam) a blockage
**Heimlich maneuver** (HYM lik  muh NOO vur) a procedure to force out food that is stuck in a choking person's throat

Unfortunately, the table is close to the edge of the stage. Too close. Tripping over my untied shoelace, I hurtle headfirst into the darkness.

My body makes some very unpleasant sounds as it lands.

Okay, I probably could have accepted the broken leg.

I might even have been able to live with the memory of the look on Tiffany's face.

But when the ambulance guys came and put me on a stretcher, and everyone stood there watching as they rolled me out of the school, and Mikey followed after them to tell me that my fly had been open during the entire fiasco, I really thought that was too much.

Anyway, that's how I ended up in this hospital bed, staring at my right leg, which is up in traction.

Tiffany came to visit a while ago. That would have been wonderful, except she brought along her boyfriend, Chuck. He goes to another school and is old enough to drive.

Something inside me died when she introduced him. **8**

> **8 Interpreting**
> What does Murphy mean when he says this?

To make things worse (and what doesn't?), it turns out that Chuck was in the audience yesterday.

"You were brilliant, man," he says. "At least, until the part where it all fell to pieces."

I want to shove a Hostess cupcake down his throat.

After they are gone, Mikey shows up.

"Tough luck, Murphy," he says, looking at my cast.

I try to remember that he is my best friend and really thought he was saving my life when he Heimliched me. It is not easy.

"Cheer up," he says. "It couldn't get worse than this."

---

## Vo•cab•u•lary

**fiasco** (fee AS koh) a complete failure

He's lucky my leg is in traction and I can't get out of bed. He is also lucky I don't have a cupcake on me.

After Mikey leaves, I make two decisions: (a) I am going to change my name and (b) I never want to be thirteen again as long as I live.

There is another knock on my door.

"Hello, Murphy," says a soft voice.

It's Laurel.

She smiles shyly. "Can I come in?"

I've never noticed how pretty she is when she smiles. For a brief moment I think life may not be so bad after all.

I am fairly certain, however, this is a <u>delusion</u>.

After all, my name is still Murphy Murphy.

And I'm still thirteen years old.

I don't even want to think about what might happen next. ○

---

## Answering the BIG Question

As you do the following activities, consider the Big Question:
**How do you keep from giving up when bad things happen?**

**WRITE TO LEARN** Think of a time when you dreaded an experience and it turned out even worse than you had feared. Write about it in your Learner's Notebook. As you look back on the experience, can you find something funny about it?

**LITERATURE GROUPS** Meet with two or three others who have read this story. Take turns reading aloud the parts of the story that you find most amusing. Would you be able to laugh if something similar happened to you?

---

## Vo·cab·u·lary

**delusion** (dih LOO zhun) a false idea

# SPRING 1954: RICHMOND, VIRGINIA

by Randall Robinson
from *Defending the Spirit:*
*A Black Life in America*

**Find out how one eighth grader reacted to change.**

At thirteen I began making deliveries for Katz Groceries at Clay and Belvidere Streets. Mr. and Mrs. Katz were solicitous and patient with their new hire, and I was earnest if only marginally efficient. I worked from four until seven-thirty weekdays, seven to seven on Saturdays, and a half day on Sundays. The store was a mile's walk from our flat, a half block north to Clay and west to Belvidere. I earned thirteen dollars a week. Mama and Daddy allowed me to keep the money to manage as I saw fit. I opened an account at Consolidated, then one of the country's oldest black banks, whose president, Mr. Nickens, was a figure of considerable community stature.

With a portion of my earnings I bought clothes, partially relieving Daddy of the burden. From Julian's Fine Clothiers on Broad Street I purchased a white-on-white cloth Billy Eckstine dress shirt with the gull-wing flying collar. I accessorized the shirt with argyle socks and a tie whose width I tailored down severely to the black community's fashion tolerance of the time. My suit and pants remained those that Max had outgrown.

At 2:30 P.M. on the afternoon of May 17, 1954, I was sitting in Mr. Bland's eighth-grade science class at the battered desk on the outside row near a bank of open windows, wearing my Billy Eckstine classic. The school was Benjamin A. Graves Junior

High, an imposing old <u>colonnaded</u> redbrick building situated on Lee Street halfway between Katz Groceries and home.

Mr. Bland was a big barrel-chested man with a booming voice and a brush mustache. Unlike the diminutive but stern Mrs. Diamond, who fixed her thirteen-year-old geometry students with "the look" before the lesson, Mr. Bland couldn't control his class. Well, in fairness, it was me and one or two others he couldn't control. Sometimes, even now, I feel a twinge of remorse about the stress I caused this large, kind man who taught science and played the violin.

"_____has just been handed down and it will change all of our lives." Mr. Bland was talking. I wasn't listening but everyone else appeared to be, which was unusual.

"What did he say?" I asked the girl in front of me. Mr. Bland heard.

"I said, Randall, that the United States Supreme Court has outlawed public school segregation. The schools will be integrated." ❶

I was stunned. The class was quiet, reactions difficult to read. If this <u>warranted</u> a celebration, it got none from Mr. Bland's science class.

**❶ Summarizing**
What did the teacher tell the class that would change their lives?

Within days, I thought, I'll be in another school with white people. I was trying to come to terms with this news, which was unsettling to say the least. I'd never expected such. Not in my lifetime.

Let me be completely honest about my memory of the effect on me of Mr. Bland's announcement. I did not want to go to school with white people. I wanted the right to go anywhere I wished to go. I also wanted the right not to go. And if the choice were mine, count me out. I'll concede that I was more than a little frightened. After all, white people had spent the better part of four hundred years conspiring to convince me of my <u>innate</u> intellectual inferiority.

---

## Vo•cab•u•lary

**colonnaded** (kaw luh NAY dud) made with columns
**warranted** (WOR unt ed) deserved
**innate** (ih NAYT) something a person is born with

They had made some headway. And I hated them for that. At thirteen, I only sometimes thought I was smart. I secretly believed I was special. I even felt, well, yes, immortal, as I later discovered many thirteen-year-olds do. But the doubts about competitive ability had been well sown. Also by age thirteen, I had <u>intuitively</u> developed the <u>cardinal</u> guidepost for emotional health: the Never Wannabe Rule. Never want to be with people who don't want to be with you. Its derivative has served me just as profitably: Never like people who don't like you. There may be occasions when you are allowed to dislike those who like you. The converse proposition, however, is <u>anathema</u>.

The bell was about to ring, sending us back to our homerooms. Mr. Bland was asking us about the characteristics of cumulus clouds.

My mind wandered. I was thinking about how white students might be accepting the news at Hermitage, Highland Springs, and Thomas Jefferson. I couldn't visualize these schools. I'd never seen them. But I pictured white faces, some tear-streaked, some angry.

*Don't flatter yourselves. I'm not coming to your school.*

I needn't have troubled. Forty-three years later, Richmond's public schools are virtually as segregated as they were that spring afternoon of Mr. Bland's bombshell.  ○

---

## Answering the BIG Question

As you do the following activities, consider the Big Question:
**How do you keep from giving up when bad things happen?**

**WRITE TO LEARN** Think about the author's reaction to the teacher's announcement. Write a brief entry in your Learner's Notebook reflecting on how you would feel if you had to go to a new school.

**LITERATURE GROUPS** Meet with two or three others who have read the selection. Discuss what you think it would have been like to be one of the first students in an integrated school.

---

## Vo·cab·u·lary

**intuitively** (in TOO uh tiv lee) known by instinct
**cardinal** (KAR duh nul) most important
**anathema** (uh NAH thuh muh) being hated

# CRASH COURSE

by Ben Shannon

**A serious accident breaks a snowboarder's arm—and her spirit.**

OOOH... WHAT HAPPENED?

SO YOU'VE FINALLY DECIDED TO WAKE UP, HMM?

WHERE AM I? WHO ARE YOU? OH YEAH, THE BOARDING COMPETITION!

I REALLY CRASHED OUT AND... OH, MY HEAD!

JUST LIE BACK AND REST, AMY. I'M DR. JACKSON. I OPERATED ON YOU AFTER YOUR ACCIDENT. I JUST FINISHED MY SHIFT, SO I THOUGHT I'D COME BY AND SEE HOW YOU'RE RECOVERING.

YOU HAD QUITE THE NASTY SPILL, YOU KNOW.

WHEN LEONARDO DA VINCI WAS JUST STARTING OUT AS A PAINTER, HE USED AN EXPERIMENTAL TECHNIQUE ON HIS NOW FAMOUS MURAL "THE LAST SUPPER."

ALMOST AS SOON AS HE FINISHED THE PAINTING IT BEGAN TO RUN AND FADE.

LEONARDO WAS CRUSHED!

I'LL BET HE WASN'T AS CRUSHED AS I WAS BY THAT JUMP.

MAYBE NOT, BUT FORTUNATELY FOR US HE WAS ABLE TO PUT THE EMBARRASSMENT OF HIS FAILURE BEHIND HIM.

HE WENT ON TO CREATE COUNTLESS BEAUTIFUL MASTERPIECES, AND ALL BECAUSE HE DIDN'T LET ONE BAD THING BREAK HIS SPIRIT.

OK, THAT'S A PRETTY INSPIRING STORY, BUT BIG DEAL. LEONARDO JUST NEEDED TO GET HIS CONFIDENCE BACK UP. HE DIDN'T HAVE TO DEAL WITH A BROKEN ARM LIKE MINE.

I KNEW IT! HE DID GO NUTS!

BEETHOVEN LOVED MUSIC SO MUCH THAT HE COULDN'T LET A LITTLE THING LIKE NOT BEING ABLE TO HEAR STOP HIM, SO HE BEGAN TO SAW THE LEGS OFF HIS FAVORITE PIANO...

HARDLY. BY SAWING OFF THE LEGS OF HIS PIANO HE COULD FEEL THE VIBRATIONS IT MADE THROUGH THE FLOOR. THAT WAY HE COULD CONTINUE TO DO WHAT HE LOVED MOST.

HE SPENT THE REST OF HIS LIFE WRITING BEAUTIFUL MUSIC. MUSIC HE COULD FEEL BUT NEVER HEAR.

**WRITE TO LEARN**
Think about someone who overcame serious problems to succeed. It could be someone you know personally or a person from history or current events. Tell this person's story as a short graphic novel in your Learner's Notebook. Draw a few frames, or cells, that show the highlights of the story. Don't forget to include dialogue.

THE END.

# Blinking

by Morton Marcus

**How can you find joy even after disaster strikes?**

You've got to love life so much that you don't want to miss a moment of it, and pay such close attention to whatever you're doing that each time you blink you can hear your eyelashes applauding what you've just seen.

In each eye there are more than 80 eyelashes, forty above and forty below, like forty pairs of arms working, 80 pairs in both eyes, a whole audience clapping so loud you can hardly bear to listen. **1**

> **1 Visualizing**
> Picture those eyelashes clapping away.

160 hands batter each other every time you blink. "Bravo!" they call. "Encore! Encore!"

Paralyzed in a hospital bed, or watching the cold rain from under a bridge—remember this.

## Vo•cab•u•lary

**encore** (ON kor) a request by the audience for an additional performance
**paralyzed** (PAR uh lyzd) unable to move

# David

by William I. Elliott

---

**People can leave a permanent impression on the world, even after they are gone.**

---

Last fall you threw the softball in the gutter
just as Dad had called us into dinner. It's still
there. So's an old cat's cradle in the apple tree
twigs had tried and failed to tie
out of kite string.
A grubby balsam glider wing still sticks
in the rot of the roof's redwood shingles.

If what we do is what we are,
you're all over the place.
You said the chimney ate your plastic boomerang.
If what we do is who we are,
you're still home
here with us;
more than underground. ❷

> ❷ **Drawing Conclusions**
> Do you think the speaker will ever forget David? Explain.

# Incident

## by Countee Cullen

**Sometimes the smallest things make the biggest impression.**

Once riding in old Baltimore,
  Heart-filled, head-filled with glee,
I saw a Baltimorean
  Keep looking straight at me.

Now I was eight and very small,
  And he was no whit bigger,
And so I smiled, but he poked out
  His tongue and called me, "Nigger."

I saw the whole of Baltimore
  From May until December:
Of all the things that happened there
  That's all that I remember. ○

## Answering the BIG Question

As you do the following activities, consider the Big Question:
**How do you keep from giving up when bad things happen?**

**WRITE TO LEARN** In the poem "David," what things help the speaker remember his brother? Do you think the speaker gets comfort from those things? Answer these questions in a brief entry in your Learner's Notebook.

**PARTNER TALK** Get together with a partner who has read these selections. Discuss your responses to the Big Question. What have these selections taught you about not giving up when bad things happen?

# BALANCE

by June A. English

**Will Sheila ever again be able to do what she loves?**

My younger sister, Sheila, lives about eight miles down the road from me now. It's hard to miss Sheila. She has a mane of wild red hair, and she's nearly six feet tall. We don't know why her hair is red or how she got to be that tall. My father is no more than five-eleven, even when he stretches, and my mom is even shorter. Virtually no one in our family has had red hair in a hundred years. Well, there was my aunt Ethel. She had carrot-red hair once, but only for a week.

I used to tease Sheila that she was adopted. I knew she wasn't, of course, since I was older. After she came home—about the fifth day, I think—I demanded that they return her to the hospital. She was a screamer from day one. When she was about three months old, I stuffed a wad of tissue paper in her mouth to keep her quiet. It wasn't a popular move, but it was one I kept considering through the years.

We shared a room and, like most sisters, had some differences of opinion—that would be the polite way of putting it. I made my bed most days, and the sheets were generally washed and fairly tidy. My sister, on the other hand, would require an <u>archaeologist</u> with <u>carbon-dating</u> <u>expertise</u> to figure out how old some of the stuff was under her bed. Baseball gloves, hockey pucks, and copies of *Sports Illustrated* were all mixed in with about a month's worth of laundry. Amid this more or less normal debris were about fifteen assorted jars of dirt from Wrigley Field and several other "incredibly important" ballparks Sheila had visited. The entire effect was like a World War I trench <u>inhabited</u> by a baseball team. **❶**

**❶ Visualizing**
Picture the room the two sisters shared.

My sister kept her favorite bat lodged just above her pillow, even though once or twice I'm sure she got a <u>concussion</u> bouncing on the mattress at the end of the day. I thought she kept it there for protection, but I found out eventually that she thought of it more like a wooden teddy bear.

Sheila was ten or so when she started playing baseball.

## Vo•cab•u•lary

**archaeologist** (ar kee AH law jist) a person who studies the past by examining old objects
**carbon-dating** (KAR bun DAYT ing) a method used to determine an object's age by measuring the amount of carbon it contains
**expertise** (ek spur TEEZ) skill or knowledge in an area
**inhabited** (in HAB uh tud) lived in
**concussion** (kun KUH shun) an injury to the brain resulting from a heavy blow

## Balance

We both started, actually, but I was a <u>dismal</u> failure. I could never seem to see the ball unless it came close enough to knock me unconscious. Sheila, on the other hand, had all the necessary skills to play the game. She could hit the ball, run like lightning, and, most important, she could get incredibly dirty. At times she was so dirty, she could have been sold as real estate. That's the truth.

My dad got us a new truck in December of 1994. I had just learned how to drive, and one of my jobs was to ferry Sheila around. I would pick her up after practice—hoping that most of the sweat would bounce off her before she got in the seat. One day she came bounding up to the truck, bat in one hand, glove in the other, with a doughnut in her mouth. It was an incredibly elegant presentation. She carefully nestled the glove and bat securely behind the seat and then stuck the honey-dipped doughnut on the dashboard.

"Do you think maybe you could find a napkin?" I asked.

"Not likely," she said, now trying to attach the doughnut to the gearshift.

"Is there any chance in our lifetimes that you'll clean yourself up?"

"I am clean. I'm just sweaty and dusty, like anybody'd be after playing for two hours. Besides, underneath all this stuff I'm just as clean as you are, maybe cleaner."

When I got home, I told my parents I wasn't picking Sheila up anymore. I told my father the experience was making me faint and I might just pass out behind the wheel. He smiled at me, but I could see he wasn't really amused.

"Part of the deal of you driving the truck is that you pick up Sheila."

"I wouldn't mind picking her up if she were like other people."

"Isn't she like other people?"

---

### Vo•cab•u•lary

**dismal** (DIZ mul) gloomy or bleak

"No, she definitely isn't. She's six foot and every single foot of her is . . . " I danced around for a word while my father looked intense. He had—basically—a thirty-second limit on any argument involving my sister and me.

"You and your sister may be chalk and cheese, but this world is big enough for both of you."

The world maybe was, if we included both hemispheres, but one room was really pushing it. ❷

When I walked upstairs, Sheila had taken a shower. There was a puddle trail from the bath into our room.

> ❷ **Drawing Conclusions**
> How did the narrator feel about Sheila?

"Did you ever think of using a towel?"

"There was only one towel. I wrapped my hair in it."

She was lying in bed, rolling around to dry off.

"By the way, you don't have to pick me up on Wednesday. Mom and Dad are coming to see the game. Our Bluebirds are playing the Pelicans. The Pelicans won the league championship last year."

"Which league is that, the league of ornithologists?"

"You could come too if you wanted."

"I think I have to write a paper on the mating habits of the dodo."

"Suit yourself."

On Wednesday night—and need I say against my will?— I was sitting in the bleachers watching Sheila's Bluebirds battle the Pelicans.

Sheila typically played the outfield, left or center. Today she was stationed deep in center. The Pelicans—she had informed us in great detail—had a lot of long-ball hitters. Sheila, true to

## Vo•cab•u•lary

**ornithologists** (or nih THAW luh jists) scientists who study birds

form, was catching everything that came within her range. She even snagged a few feathers from one of the pigeons that flew over her head.

It was the botttom of the eighth, and the Pelicans—who were never far behind—were threatening. A walk and a double had left Pelicans on second and third. Another long ball and the Bluebirds would lose their lead. Sheila, who had played the game near the fence, closed in on the infield.

"She hates when she can't play deep," said my father knowingly. Unlike the rest of us, he understood Sheila.

The Bluebird pitcher was tense. She was chewing her gum especially hard and blowing large bubbles between pitches. On a 3-and-0 count, she let go with a high hard one. The Pelican batter smacked at the ball, which was high enough to drop behind Sheila. She ran back for it, her long arm reaching. I could almost see her willing it into her glove. As she grabbed it, she stumbled on a clump of grass. I expected her to fall, but somehow she didn't. Even without the ground to rely on, she balanced herself, pivoted, and in one elegant movement powered the ball to home plate. The catcher had plenty of time to block the plate and tag the runner. ❸

❸ **Visualizing**
Picture Sheila's amazing grace and skill!

My parents, as well as everyone else, were on their feet, raving. People were shouting Sheila's name. I sat on the bleachers, wondering: how did she do that? How could she pivot and throw that ball, without a foot on the ground?

We got home and had Sheila's favorite snack: Mountain Dew and Doritos. Dad promised her she could drive the tractor the next day.

Dad had a new John Deere <u>combine</u> that he used mostly, but he kept his old tractor around "just in case." Sheila would take

---

## Vo•cab•u•lary

**combine** (KAWM byn) a machine used to harvest grain

it out now and then, running it over the fields when they were seeding. He only let her use it on flat ground. The Beast—as he called it—had a tendency to <u>bank</u> wildly.

Sheila was up early and out the door. Dad had left even earlier to see about something at the farm up the road. Sheila started the Beast herself. The thing shook the ground like an angry brontosaurus. Ma was making breakfast and singing to herself. She was breaking eggs in a pan when we heard a noise like a shot. We stared at each other and started to laugh. The Beast was at least thirty years old. We figured the engine had just shut down. When we stopped laughing, though, we could still hear the grinding of gears.

"Go out there and see what's going on with that thing. And tell your sister to come in for breakfast. Tell her to leave that Beast alone till your dad comes back."

I ran out the back door to the little hill behind our house. I could see the old tractor, but it had rolled over and was turned on its side. I screamed for Ma and ran to see where Sheila was.

## Vo•cab•u•lary
**bank** (bangk) rise up or tilt

## Balance

As soon as I got near the cab, I saw that she was still inside. I climbed up on the side of the tractor.

Her face was turned away from me. "Get out of there," I said, knocking my fist on the glass window. When she turned toward me, I could tell she was in trouble. Her face was white—gray-white—like dirty snow, framed in a tangle of red hair.

My mother was behind me now. "Get your father," she said, and pushed me hard in the direction of the neighbor's field.

I ran as fast as I could. My lungs hurt with the effort, and I thought furiously how Sheila could have run so much faster. I found my father but was so out of breath I had no voice. I just said, "Sheila," and started to cry.

We got in the neighbor's truck. On the way I started breathing again and told him she was still in the tractor. We drove fast down the road, and I felt myself sweating in the seat. The rivers of it rolled off my legs, and I could see the sweat on my father's temples. When we got back to the tractor, my mother had gotten the passenger side open and was holding Sheila's hand.

"Her leg is caught," my mother said, staring hard at my father. "She's in a lot of pain."

As if in agreement, Sheila let out a long moan. I never had heard her in pain before. It sounded terrible.

My dad was shaking his head, like he was trying to clear it to think. "I can't do this myself," he said. "I might hurt her worse. Call the paramedics. Tell them we might need something to get through metal. Tell them it's an old tractor."

We waited there with Sheila for the long minutes before the paramedics came with a fire truck. The firefighters cut through the metal, and they slowly pulled Sheila out of the tractor. Her legs were dangling at strange angles, and one was bleeding. They put her neck in a brace and strapped her legs to a board. ❹

When they put her in the ambulance, she had IVs hanging off of her and was still so white, I thought she

❹ **Summarizing**
In a few sentences, tell what happened after the narrator saw the overturned tractor.

was going to die for sure. I looked hard at one of the paramedics as they loaded her into the ambulance. He must have known what I was thinking. "She'll be okay," he said. "It's all right."

I don't know if they are trained to say stuff like that, but it made me feel better. Ma and Dad went with the ambulance, but they made me stay home, "in case something happens." I couldn't believe it. I wanted to go with Sheila. I sat staring at the blank television screen for two hours before they called to say Sheila was going to be all right. She had broken bones in both her legs and crushed an ankle, but they could fix her.

I had dreamed so many times of having the room we shared to myself. That night I had my wish, but I couldn't sleep without her being there. I found myself staring at that baseball bat above her pillow. Eventually I fell asleep on her bed.

The next day my parents took me with them to the hospital. Sheila was still white, but she looked less slushy and was even smiling a little. It was startling to see her with casts on both her legs. And even more startling to see her so clean.

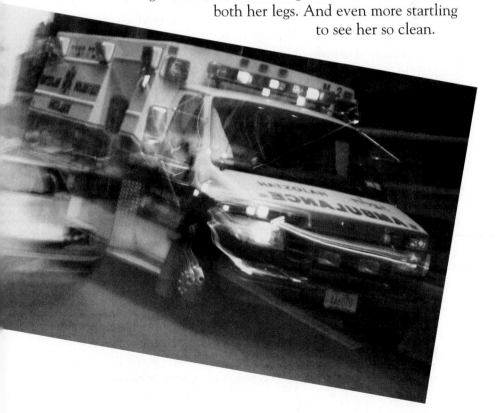

"Dad said you're going to have to take a defensive driving course before he lets you use another of his tractors."

Sheila laughed. The rocking of her body, though, sent a spasm of pain through her and she <u>grimaced</u> a little.

"Do you want me to bring you your baseball bat so you have something to hug at night?"

"Maybe you better wait," said Sheila. She looked tired. I sat next to her bed for a while, eating the hospital Jell-O she'd left on her dinner tray. "They said it will be months before I can even walk."

"Well, that's normal. I mean . . . you did really break some stuff."

"Actually, what they said was that one of my legs may be a little short."

"You're too tall anyway. What's an inch or two?"

I thought that was funny, but Sheila didn't laugh. She just shut her eyes and said she wanted to sleep. I went down to the lobby and found my parents. We got in the car and started the long drive back to the farm. The silence in the car made me uncomfortable.

"Sheila says she may end up shorter. I told her that might be an improvement."

My father gave me a hard look. ❺ I looked at my mother for a reprieve.

"Her ankle was crushed," she said. "They don't think they can fix it to be exactly the same."

❺ **Interpreting**
Why did the narrator's father give her a "hard look"?

"They can fix it, though," I said. "She'll be able to walk and everything."

My father stared straight ahead. His voice was quiet, but there was this tiny shake in it. "She can't run anymore."

## Vo•cab•u•lary

**grimaced** (GRIM ust) made a facial expression of disgust or pain

I sat back in the car seat and looked out the window. I tried to picture Sheila not running in my mind, but that picture wouldn't come. Instead I kept seeing the image of Sheila catching that fly ball and pivoting on thin air.

A week later Sheila was home. For the next six months she went every week to <u>rehab</u>, where they taught her how to walk again. She was brave about it and determined, although she wouldn't go to the games anymore. Ma and Dad kept encouraging her to go—just to see her friends. But she kept shaking them off. The baseball season ended, and through the winter Sheila kept up her rehab. Her legs got stronger, but she had a slight limp, and the doctors told her she would have to get some corrective shoes to <u>compensate</u> for the shortness in her left leg.

By spring Sheila could walk around almost like a normal person. She didn't have all that much to entertain herself, though, so she cut her hair and began painting her nails. She even started cleaning her room. I think she thought I would appreciate her effort, but it kind of unbalanced me. I found myself throwing my clothes around so the place would look normal again.

The coach at school kept calling, asking Sheila to come to the Bluebirds' opening game. She refused at first, but eventually she grudgingly said okay. We all went with her. I watched Sheila's face as all the Bluebirds lined up before the game and wondered how it could be that she wasn't standing with them. She seemed okay, though, staring straight ahead and clapping for them as they took the field. We sang the national anthem, and the coach came out and introduced the players. He said he'd like someone

---

## Vo·cab·u·lary

**rehab** (REE hab) a medical facility that helps people heal from injuries or disease
**compensate** (KAWM pun sayt) to make up for

to throw out the first ball of the season. Then he brought the ball over to the stands and handed it to Sheila.

I don't think I ever saw Sheila drop a ball before, but she dropped that one. She dug it up out of the dirt, though, and walked to the mound. She stood there for a while in silence, and we all wondered if maybe this was just too much for her. But she finally kicked her leg, drew back her arm, and let the ball fly. It was a clean strike.

Sheila never became a real pitcher. Her leg wouldn't allow her to cover first base fast enough. She did pitch relief in a couple of games, though, and ended up with a winning record. By the close of the season I had a boyfriend and I took him to watch one of the Bluebirds' last games. The game went into extra innings, and Sheila pitched the last two. He studied her on the mound for a while, her hands tarred up and her red hair flying. Finally he shook his head and laughed. "Your sister's nothing like you," he said. "I can't believe it."

I had heard that so many times in my life and never knew what to say. This time, though, I didn't even have to think about it.

"True, but there's room enough for both of us," I said, "even in just this hemisphere." **6** ○

**6 Drawing Conclusions** How have the narrator's feelings about Sheila changed since the accident?

**Answering the BIG Question**

As you do the following activities, consider the Big Question:
**How do you keep from giving up when bad things happen?**

**WRITE TO LEARN** How do you think Sheila would answer the Big Question? Write a brief entry in your Learner's Notebook.

**LITERATURE GROUPS** Meet with two or three others who have read "Balance." Discuss how you think the relationship between the two sisters changed after Sheila's accident.

# Maximum Pressure

## teens face stress every day

by Nancy Fitzgerald

**Discover how to keep stress from getting the best of you.**

**S**pencer Patterson is stressed out. He crawls out of bed at 6 a.m., travels an hour and a half to school, and makes his way through a day of demanding classes. His day is so full that he doesn't have time to eat lunch. After school, he attends rehearsals for school plays. And then there's the two-hour trip home.

Evenings are filled with chores, martial arts classes, and homework. Late at night he works on his comedy routines, which he performs on weekends in New York. "Sometimes I just feel overstressed," says Spencer, 15, a freshman at the Frank Sinatra School for the Arts in Queens, New York.

Welcome to Spencer's world. It's probably a little bit like yours. According to a recent study by the University of Minnesota, 39 percent of American teens report feeling stressed during a typical day.

## Oh, the Pressure

"Kids today are under more stress than previous generations," says Erika Karres, Ph.D., a <u>psychologist</u> and <u>editor</u> of *Mean Chicks, Cliques, and Dirty Tricks* (Adams Media, 2004). "There are pressures from family situations and <u>economic</u> factors. Kids hear parents

---

### Vo•cab•u•lary

**psychologist** (sy KAW luh jist) a person who studies the ways people act, think, and feel

**editor** (EH duh tur) a person who checks the text of a book, newspaper, or magazine

**economic** (ek uh NAW mik) related to a person's or the country's financial state

worrying about jobs. They may have responsibility for younger <u>siblings</u>. They're under pressure to do well in school and get into <u>top-notch</u> colleges. They're under stress to wear the right clothes, <u>excel</u> in sports, and even volunteer in their communities."

Believe it or not, stress is nothing new. Our ancestors developed a fight-or-flight reaction to danger thousands of years ago. When danger crossed their paths—a wild animal, a hostile band of warriors, or a violent storm—their bodies were flooded with natural chemicals that put them on alert. When the danger passed, the chemicals subsided, the stress was gone, and life went back to normal. ❶

**❶ Paraphrasing**
How would you explain the fight-or-flight reaction to a younger student?

Fast forward to the 21st century. For teens like Spencer, the stressors are different—they take the form of academic overload and family worries rather than attacks by wild boars. But the troubling thing for teens today is that often the stressors don't go away.

## Body Assault

"When you experience stress, your body and brain are in a heightened state to manage whatever the event is," explains Dr. Philippe Cunningham, associate professor of <u>psychiatry</u> at the Medical University of South Carolina in Charleston. "But your body needs a chance to recover. The more stressors there are—and the longer they last—the more likely you are to feel overwhelmed by them. It's like running a race that doesn't end."

All that stress can lead to physical symptoms such as headaches, stomachaches, sweating, sleeplessness, and constant fatigue. Constant stress can lead to potentially serious conditions like irregular heartbeats and high blood pressure. Stress can also cause emotional problems such as anxiety, anger, hostility, and depression.

---

## Vo•cab•u•lary

**siblings** (SIH blings) brothers and sisters
**top-notch** (tawp nawch) excellent
**excel** (ik SEL) do very well
**psychiatry** (sy KY uh tree) the branch of medicine related to mental health

# Stress Busters

There are many ways to cope with stress. Here are six that may help you:

Relax—The following techniques can help you calm down: deep breathing, yoga, meditation, or prayer. "Before taking a test, I tried the meditation technique they taught us at school," says Jared Williams, 14, of Detroit, Michigan. "I sat down and closed my eyes and it really helped. My grade in class went up from a D to a C."

Talk to Someone—Open up to a trusted adult—a parent, teacher, or guidance counselor. "The more you depend on yourself, the more out of control things get," says Dr. Philippe Cunningham. "You need to ask an adult for help." Expressing your feelings in a journal may also help.

Work Out—When you exercise, your body releases a calming hormone called endorphin. Katelyn Helgason, 17, of Grand Forks, North Dakota, has a demanding course load, household

Some kids turn to alcohol and drugs to help them cope with stress. "That may allow teens to escape the stress for the moment, but it doesn't help them deal with stress," Cunningham says.

Spencer is working on ways to reduce his stress. For instance, math is his most challenging subject. He works with a tutor on his math assignments and asks his math-savvy friends for help after class. When he's upset and needs an outlet, Spencer often rides his bicycle or hits a punching bag in the basement of his home.  ○

chores, homework, and a part-time job. But most evenings, she runs laps, lifts weights, or shoots baskets. "It helps me relax and sleep better at night," she says.

Have Fun—Take time to do things that you enjoy. The evenings of Brittany Birckett, 14, of Modesto, California, are packed with activities. But she sets aside an hour every day to grab a snack, talk on the phone, and watch TV. "It really helps me wind down," Brittany says. And on most Friday nights she goes to the movies with friends.

Manage Your Time—"Plan ahead," says psychologist Erika Karres. "Break tasks down into manageable pieces. If you're doing a term paper, visit the library one night, take notes the second, write an outline the third."

Be with Positive People—A great way to learn to cope with stress is to watch others do it. If your parents show grace under pressure, pay attention to what they do and copy their example. And if you've got friends who freak out at the first sign of stress, find new friends. **2**

**2 Summarizing**
What are six good ways to deal with stress?

## Answering the
## BIG Question

As you do the following activities, consider the Big Question:
**How do you keep from giving up when bad things happen?**

**WRITE TO LEARN** Think about the stress busters described in this article. Write a brief entry in your Learner's Notebook about the stress busters you have tried and how they worked for you.

**LITERATURE GROUPS** Meet with two or three others who have read "Maximum Pressure." Discuss what you have learned about stress and how to manage it.

# Kemba's
## STORY

How do you get through times of loss?

I enjoy going on Mission's trips with my church. I've been on two to Brazil. I'm probably going back there next summer. I'm very active in the church. My father is one of the pastors. And that's where a lot of my friends are.

Sports mean a lot of things to me. It's kind of a way of escaping the pressures of the real world, because it's kind of like a fantasy world. If I'm having a problem with a friend or a problem at home, and I have a basketball game in two hours, then I quickly forget about my problems. I just focus on the game and winning. I have fun with my team.

Being an adolescent is a very hard thing to be nowadays. There are a lot of pressures in the media to look a certain way or act a certain way. If a teenager or a pre-teen doesn't act in that way, then they put themselves down, and they could be very upset at themselves. **❶**

**❶ Interpreting**
Use your own words to explain what Kemba is saying in this paragraph.

I'd say the hardest thing that I went through when I was growing up, was probably my mother dying. My mother was <u>diagnosed</u> with breast cancer. She had to go through <u>chemotherapy</u>. The cancer had moved to her lungs. She couldn't breathe. She only used a certain percentage of her lungs. It was really hard on her and the whole family. One day she died. We called her funeral a home-going rather than a funeral, because she went on to heaven.

I didn't cry until a couple of months after. I was at school. I had to go to a social worker and talk about my problems. Then I would cry sometimes. There was about a month of that. After that, I talked about my problems and I got them out.

My relationship with my dad is a really close one. Since my mother's not here, I have to <u>confide</u> in him. I talk to him a lot. I don't withhold anything from him. I can cry. I can laugh with him. I think that's a really important relationship.

I think that my father will help me, in my relationship with

## Vo•cab•u•lary

**diagnosed** (DY ig nohsd) determined what disease a person has
**chemotherapy** (kee moh THAIR uh pee) a medical treatment that uses chemicals to kill cancer cells
**confide** (kun FYD) to tell something in confidence

# Kemba's Story

other men, because he could give me advice or he could be there. If I have questions about someone I'm seeing or something like that, I can always turn to him.

I think my dad builds my confidence a lot. He confides in me sometimes. He thinks I'm really responsible and smart. So when he tells me these things, and when he congratulates me, and rewards me for something I did, I get excited about myself, and I feel really happy about myself.

My spirituality plays a very big role in my life. My dad gives me a strong basis for relying on God, and everything will be OK. That's what I believe.

Two women stepped up a lot at my church during my times of need. When my mother was sick, they would take me out and drive for two hours somewhere and just have long talks about what was going on with my mother. That really helped me a lot. It let me know that people were supporting me. They also gave me a sense of comfort, which I think was really important at that time.

I think that these women have given me a basis to help others I see

Dealing with It—Remember that it's normal to feel deep sadness, anger, or confusion when you've experienced a loss. Different people respond differently to loss.

Even if you think no one will understand, tell an adult you trust what you are feeling.

Kemba says, although she will always miss her mom, she feels better again.

Kemba knows her mother would want her to be doing things that she enjoys, like playing basketball and being with her friends.

Sometimes it helps to write down what you are feeling. Some young people who've lost loved ones say it helps to write that person a letter.

in need. Like if I see a little girl or a little boy whose parent may be sick or has just died, then I know how to talk to them. I know what to say, and I know what not to say, too. ○

## Answering the BIG Question

As you do the following activities, consider the Big Question:
**How do you keep from giving up when bad things happen?**

**WRITE TO LEARN** Think about the things that helped Kemba deal with her mother's death. Write a brief entry in your Learner's Notebook, reflecting on what helps you get through the toughest times in your life.

**PARTNER TALK** Meet with a partner who has read "Kemba's Story." Discuss these questions: How can you help a person who is grieving? What would you want others to do if you were grieving? Determine which strategies would be helpful for kids facing other types of problems.

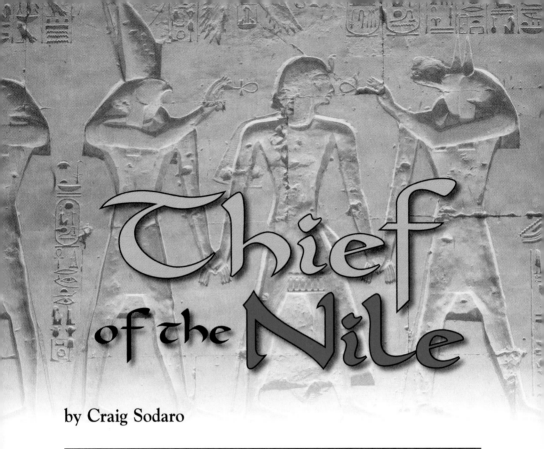

# Thief of the Nile

by Craig Sodaro

**A servant girl in ancient Egypt finds herself with an agonizing choice: poison the pharaoh or risk being killed.**

## Characters

**Tem:** The Pharaoh's favorite wife

**Nyla:** Servant girl

**Peshet:** Servant girl

**Rahotep:** Royal vizier

**Mentuhotep:** The Pharaoh

**Inu:** The wife of Pharaoh's architect

**General Nefermenu**

## Vo•cab•u•lary

**Pharaoh's** (FAIR ohz) belonging to a king of ancient Egypt
**vizier** (vuh ZEER) a high government official in ancient Egypt
**architect** (AR kih tekt) a person who designs buildings

## Scene 1

**Time:** 2055 B.C.

**Setting:** Palace of the Pharaoh Mentuhotep in <u>Thebes</u>. A bench or two at center with a railing upstage. Beyond railing, a suggestion of the desert, perhaps a palm tree or two in the distance. Several plants and pillars, if desired.

**At Rise:** Tem sits on bench, holding hand mirror. Peshet holds a box of jewelry. Nyla helps Tem try various pieces on. ❶

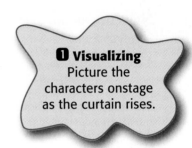

❶ **Visualizing**
Picture the characters onstage as the curtain rises.

**Tem.** (*appraising a new necklace*) And what do we think, my two turtledoves?

**Nyla.** It is not for us to say, your highness.

**Tem.** Oh, come, come, Nyla. You are more than a servant to me. You are like my sister.

**Peshet.** (*pertly*) In that case, I must say it's not worthy of you, your highness.

**Tem.** (*disappointed*) But Peshet, it's made of the finest gold, and these seashells—

**Peshet.** But the design looks awkward on your highness. Your neck is long and beautiful, and this necklace doesn't take advantage of that.

**Tem.** Flattery will get you everywhere.

**Peshet.** (*holding up a necklace with a sun on it*) What about this, your highness? (Nyla *gasps slightly when she sees the necklace.*)

**Tem.** (*concerned*) Are you all right, Nyla?

---

## Vo•cab•u•lary

**Thebes** (theebz) a city in ancient Egypt on the Nile River
**appraising** (uh PRAY zing) inspecting something to determine its value or worth

**Nyla.** (*nervously*) Oh, yes, your highness. Please forgive me!

**Tem.** Let's try it on. (Peshet *puts necklace around* Tem's *neck.*)

**Peshet.** (*pleased*) That is much better, your highness.

**Tem.** Where did this piece come from?

**Peshet.** I don't know. It was at the bottom of the box.

**Tem.** I like it. What do you think, Nyla?

**Nyla.** (*in hushed tones*) It is the most beautiful necklace I have ever seen.

**Tem.** I think so, too. I will keep it. (Mentuhotep *enters right, carrying a scroll.* Rahotep *follows him in.*)

**Mentuhotep.** (*shaking head; frowning*) It doesn't make sense, Rahotep!

**Rahotep.** But, your highness, the accounts are accurate.

**Mentuhotep.** (*upset*) The <u>treasury</u> has been severely <u>depleted</u>! We are facing a terrible <u>deficit</u>!

**Rahotep.** I am afraid the tax collectors have become very <u>lax</u> in their duties.

**Mentuhotep.** Even if they have, we have fought no wars, we have not undertaken any major building projects. This cannot be!

**Rahotep.** I'm afraid several of the governors may well be . . .

**Mentuhotep.** May well be what?

**Tem.** (*nodding*) Stealing, my lord. I've warned you.

**Mentuhotep.** I have appointed each governor myself!

---

## Vo•cab•u•lary

**treasury** (TREH zhu ree) the place where a government keeps its money
**depleted** (dih PLEET id) emptied out
**deficit** (DEF uh sit) shortage
**lax** (laks) relaxed; lacking strictness

**Tem.** But you know how some people always take advantage.

**Mentuhotep.** Then we will find whoever is cheating the royal treasury and make them pay. Dearly. ❷

**❷ Summarizing**
Why is Mentuhotep so upset?

**Rahotep.** Yes, your highness.

**Tem.** My lord husband, tell me what you think of this necklace. I wanted something new for the temple dedication—

**Mentuhotep.** Nothing new until these accounts are accurate, my lady. Come, Rahotep, we will have the scribes write to each governor demanding a meeting here in Thebes within the month.

**Rahotep.** Very good, your highness. (Mentuhotep *and* Rahotep *exit left.*)

**Tem.** (*as she removes necklace*) Well, my turtledoves, it doesn't look as if I can choose today. (*hands necklace to* Peshet, *who puts it back in box*)

**Peshet.** Or any day soon, my lady.

**Tem.** I'll just have to turn on the charm and convince the king I need this necklace.

**Peshet.** And the others?

**Tem.** Send them back. I need only one at the temple dedication. The people must see their queen at her radiant best, yes?

**Nyla.** (*quietly*) Yes, your highness.

**Tem.** What is wrong, dear Nyla? Your smile is gone.

**Nyla.** It is nothing.

**Tem.** Go. Rest. Peshet can help me.

**Nyla.** Yes, your highness. I shall take the jewlery back to your <u>chamber</u>.

---

## Vo·cab·u·lary

**chamber** (CHAYM bur) a room or group of rooms

**Peshet.** I can do it.

**Nyla.** But you are going to the baths. It's out of your way.

**Peshet.** Then if it's not too much trouble.

**Nyla.** Your highness. (Nyla *bows as* Tem *and* Peshet *exit left. Nyla sets box on bench and pulls the sun necklace from it. She clutches it in her hand, picks up box and rises, moving right.* Rahotep *enters left.*)

**Rahotep.** What have we here, Nyla?

**Nyla.** (*frightened*) My lord! I thought you had left!

**Rahotep.** (*slyly*) I told him I had forgotten something. He can deal with the scribes himself. More importantly, my dear, what are you doing?

**Nyla.** This is the new jewelry our queen was selecting, your grace.

**Rahotep.** Beautiful jewelry, isn't it?

**Nyla.** Yes, your grace.

**Rahotep.** Worth a great deal of money.

**Nyla.** Of course.

**Rahotep.** A single piece could make a poor servant girl's life very pleasant for a long time, could it not?

**Nyla.** (*nervously*) I suppose it would, your grace. Now, if you will excuse me, I must put these pieces away. (Nyla *attempts to push past* Rahotep, *but he grabs her arm. The sun necklace falls to the floor.*)

**Rahotep.** All but this one piece, I see!

**Nyla.** I don't know what you mean! (Rahotep *picks up necklace.*)

**Rahotep.** (*fingering the necklace*) It is very beautiful.

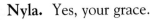

**Nyla.** Yes, your grace.

**Rahotep.** An excellent choice for you to steal.

**Nyla.** But, your grace—

**Rahotep.** Oh, don't try to deny it. I watched you the entire time. You have seen this piece of jewelry before, haven't you?

**Nyla.** Please, your grace—

**Rahotep.** *(in commanding tone)* You've seen it before!

**Nyla.** *(reluctantly)* Yes.

**Rahotep.** Where?

**Nyla.** It was my mother's.

**Rahotep.** *(surprised)* Your mother's?

**Nyla.** Yes, a gift from my father.

**Rahotep.** We shall have to ask your parents about this, then.

**Nyla.** They are both dead, your grace.

**Rahotep.** How unfortunate.

**Nyla.** The necklace was <u>entombed</u> with my mother.

**Rahotep.** But . . . that would mean her tomb has been robbed.

**Nyla.** A <u>desecration</u>! ❸

**Rahotep.** Unfortunately, no one will believe you.

**Nyla.** But it's true!

> **❸ Interpreting**
> What does Nyla mean when she calls the theft a desecration?

---

## Vo·cab·u·lary

**entombed** (in TOOMD) buried in a tomb or grave
**desecration** (deh sih KRAY shun) an act that shows disrespect for something sacred or holy

**Rahotep.** (*smugly*) What I saw was a servant girl stealing a royal necklace.

**Nyla.** (<u>*vehemently*</u>) No! It's not like that!

**Rahotep.** No one of your class would own a necklace like this.

**Nyla.** My father was an <u>artisan</u>. He made this piece for my mother.

**Rahotep.** A nice fantasy, my dear, but nothing more. I'm afraid I shall have to call the guards.

**Nyla.** (*in disbelief*) But I will be <u>cast</u> into prison.

**Rahotep.** Or worse.

**Nyla.** The Pharaoh will listen to reason. He is a kind and merciful king.

**Rahotep.** Oh, but, my dear, the Pharaoh will never even know about this. Nor will the queen. I shall simply tell them you ran off in the night to marry a young man. It happens so often, they won't bat an eye.

**Nyla.** (*near tears*) Why are you doing this to me?

**Rahotep.** For a very good reason. I need someone to do a job for me.

**Nyla.** I will do nothing for you.

**Rahotep.** (*coldly*) You will do anything and everything the Rahotep commands. You see, my child, I am the real power in this palace. I can allow you to stay here in peace and contentment, or I can have you killed. The choice is mine.

**Nyla.** (*terrified*) What . . . what am I to do?

---

## Vo•cab•u•lary

**vehemently** (VEE uh munt lee) with strong feeling
**artisan** (AR tih zun) a skilled craftsperson
**cast** (kast) thrown

**Rahotep.** *(taking vial from his belt)* Tomorrow, when you serve the king his morning drink, you will serve it with the contents of this vial.

**Nyla.** What is it?

**Rahotep.** That is not your worry.

**Nyla.** It's poison, isn't it?

**Rahotep.** It's not your concern.

**Nyla.** But everyone will know I put it there! I will be killed on the spot!

**Rahotep.** If you do as I say, I will protect you.

**Nyla.** And if I don't?

**Rahotep.** You will be killed for stealing the royal jewels. I can assure you of that! *(He puts vial in her hand and closes her fingers around it.)* There's a good girl. And don't worry, I will protect you.

**Nyla.** That is what I'm afraid of! *(Nyla hurries off right with vial and jewelry box. Rahotep holds up necklace and smiles as the curtain falls.)* ❹

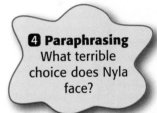

**❹ Paraphrasing**
What terrible choice does Nyla face?

## Scene 2

**Time:** A few minutes later.

**Setting:** A hallway in the palace, played before the curtain.

**At Rise:** Old Man sits on floor. He wears a robe and hood so his face is not visible at all. Nyla, carrying jewelry box and vial, enters left.

**Old Man.** *(in a disguised voice)* Who comes?

**Nyla.** *(surprised)* Oh! How did you get in the palace?

**Old Man.** It is my home.

**Nyla.** I have never seen you before.

**Old Man.** Mentuhotep's palace is very big. There are many places to hide.

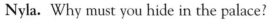

**Nyla.** Why must you hide in the palace?

**Old Man.** To keep an eye on things.

**Nyla.** What things?

**Old Man.** I know, for example, you have been crying.

**Nyla.** (*nervously*) I . . . I have something in my eye.

**Old Man.** Perhaps it was your conversation with the royal vizier Rahotep.

**Nyla.** No! And you go away or I'll call the guards!

**Old Man.** (*calmly*) They will not <u>heed</u> you.

**Nyla.** (*calling off*) Guards! Guards!

**Old Man.** (*after a pause*) You see? Tell me what the Rahotep said.

**Nyla.** I can't!

**Old Man.** For you to be so upset, he has threatened you, hasn't he?

**Nyla.** Leave me alone! (Nyla *crosses right.*)

**Old Man.** What has he asked you to do?

**Nyla.** Nothing!

**Old Man.** Nothing? All of these tears shed for nothing? You are not telling me the truth.

**Nyla.** Who are you that I should tell you the truth?

**Old Man.** Someone very close to the king.

**Nyla.** Then why would you be concerned with a lowly servant girl?

**Old Man.** You are not lowly. You are handmaid to the queen. And more important, all the king's subjects are important to him.

---

## Vo•cab•u•lary
**heed** (heed) pay attention

**Nyla.** Even those who wish him harm?

**Old Man.** Would they not be important to you if you were king?

**Nyla.** Yes, I suppose they would.

**Old Man.** And so . . . the Rahotep wishes to do harm to the king?

**Nyla.** Please! I have said more than I should!

**Old Man.** Do whatever it is that the Rahotep has asked you to do tomorrow.

**Nyla.** But I . . . I can't!

**Old Man.** Have no fear. You will be protected.

**Nyla.** That is exactly what he told me, too.

**Old Man.** Then you must decide whom to trust. **5**

**Nyla.** (*in desperate tone*) If I do what he wants . . .

**Old Man.** There is nothing to fear.

**Nyla.** Only for my life! (Nyla *exits right as lights dim to darkness.*)

> **5 Summarizing**
> In a few sentences, summarize Nyla's conversation with the Old Man.

## Scene 3

**Time:** The following morning.

**Setting:** Same as Scene 1.

**At Rise:** Mentuhotep sits on bench. Tem stands right with Peshet. Nyla stands down left.

**Tem.** (*upset*) Where is it, Peshet?

**Peshet.** I gave the jewelry to Nyla, your highness.

**Tem.** What did you do with the necklace, Nyla?

**Mentuhotep.** (*harshly*) Speak, girl!

**Nyla.** Your highness—

**Mentuhotep.** Do you know the punishment for stealing from your queen?

**Nyla.** But, your highness . . .

**Tem.** Oh, stop bullying the girl, my lord! There is more to this than meets the eye. Anyone can see that. You took only the one piece, Nyla. Why would you do such a thing? (*Rahotep enters right, attempting to stop Inu from entering.*)

**Rahotep.** The king cannot be disturbed!

**Inu.** But I have a message for his highness.

**Rahotep.** I will decide whom the king sees!

**Mentuhotep.** What is this about, Rahotep?

**Rahotep.** It is nothing that I cannot handle, your highness.

**Inu.** My husband said that I am to speak to the king personally.

**Mentuhotep.** Who is your husband?

**Inu.** He is one of the royal architects.

**Mentuhotep.** Is this true, Rahotep?

**Rahotep.** It is, your highness, but her husband is of low rank, and whatever she has to say, she can tell me and I will handle it. Surely there are more important things that your highness must tend to.

**Tem.** (*suspiciously*) There is something in your insistence that is disturbing, Vizier. ❻ Let her come forth.

> ❻ **Paraphrasing**
> Restate this sentence in your own words.

**Rahotep.** But your highness . . .

**Mentuhotep.** Do as your queen commands. (*Rahotep stands aside. Inu passes to center.*)

**Inu.** I am grateful, your highness.

**Mentuhotep.** What is your husband's message, my good woman? (*Inu looks around, suspiciously.*) You may speak freely. All here are well-trusted.

**Nyla.** But your highness—

**Tem.** Even Nyla and Peshet.

**Inu.** Very well, your highness. Yesterday my husband passed by the tomb of your mother—

**Rahotep.** Surely a lowly architect cannot even know the location of your mother's tomb, my king!

**Inu.** My husband is not lowly. He helped design and build the queen's tomb. And in passing by it, he noticed a scar in the land near the entrance. Upon examining it, he saw that someone had dug a new entrance to the tomb, loosely covered by brambles and stones.

**Tem.** *(shocked)* What?!

**Mentuhotep.** *(in disbelief)* That is <u>sacrilege</u>!

**Tem.** No living being shall <u>defile</u> the tomb of the dead.

**Rahotep.** But there are so many grave robbers loose in the kingdom.

**Mentuhotep.** What do you know of grave robbers, Rahotep?

**Rahotep.** Your highness, I had hoped to spare you such information, but a number of tombs have been robbed lately. (General Nefermenu *enters right.*) Is that not true, General Nefermenu?

**Mentuhotep.** What brings you to the palace, General?

**General.** *(bowing)* Your highness.

---

## Vo·cab·u·lary

**sacrilege** (SAK ruh lij) a desecration; an act that shows disrespect for something sacred or holy

**defile** (dih FYL) make unclean or unholy

**Rahotep.** This woman brought up another in the recent rash of grave robbings, General.

**General.** Unfortunately there have been many lately.

**Inu.** But this isn't about a robbery.

**Tem.** You said the tomb had been defiled.

**Inu.** Indeed!

**Mentuhotep.** What is missing? The stolen items must be returned so my mother's journey to the afterlife may be easy and comfortable!

**Inu.** Nothing is missing.

**General.** Inu speaks the truth.

**Rahotep.** This is all ridiculous nonsense!

**Mentuhotep.** Give me the rest of the message, Inu.

**Inu.** Yes, your highness. My husband contacted General Nefermenu and the royal guard entered the tomb.

**Mentuhotep.** Do you know what you have done?

**Rahotep.** Such desecration will cost you your life, General! (*to* Inu) And the life of your husband as well! Shall I order the guard to take these two away, your highness? **7**

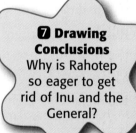

**7 Drawing Conclusions**
Why is Rahotep so eager to get rid of Inu and the General?

**General.** Please, your highness. We entered on a suspicion.

**Mentuhotep.** What suspicion?

**General.** My men have not been paid in two months. They are becoming uneasy, and uneasy soldiers are very dangerous.

**Rahotep.** You know we are struggling through low taxes and some obvious thefts from the treasury at the frontier.

**Mentuhotep.** Let them finish, Vizier.

**Tem.** What did you find when you entered the tomb, General?

**General.** We found more treasure than was placed at burial. Your husband confirmed this, Inu.

**Inu.** He said that there are ingots of gold stored up in baskets.

**Mentuhotep.** Ingots of gold!

**General.** From the treasury, your highness.

**Mentuhotep.** So, someone has been stealing gold from the treasury and hiding it in my mother's tomb?

**General.** I am afraid so, your highness.

**Inu.** But who would do such a thing?

**Mentuhotep.** Inu, you have shown courage and persistence in coming here, and have done the kingdom a great service. Tell your husband that upon removal of the gold from the tomb, he is to reseal the tomb with the help of the priests. He will receive a reward from his king personally.

**Inu.** Thank you, your highness.

**Rahotep.** I will show Inu out, your highness.

**Tem.** No! Peshet, you show Inu out.

**Mentuhotep.** You must stay, Vizier.

**Rahotep.** As you wish.

**Peshet.** This way, my lady. (Inu *bows to* Mentuhotep *and exits right with* Peshet.)

**Mentuhotep.** You can assure your men they will be paid today, General Nefermenu. Isnt't that right, Vizier?

**Rahotep.** If indeed this gold exists and is actually from the treasury.

**Mentuhotep.** You have a point.

**General.** But, your highness, surely—

**Mentuhotep.** (*raising hand, silencing* General) I am thirsty, Nyla. Bring me something to drink. (Nyla, *terrified, looks first from* Mentuhotep, *then to* Rahotep, *who nods slightly.* Nyla *bows, then exits left.*)

**Tem.** This, then, could be the answer to why the treasury is so depleted.

**Mentuhotep.** It is possible. But who would do such a thing? I have surrounded myself with only the most loyal aides. (*to* General *and* Rahotep) If I didn't trust you, I would have to sneak about the palace in disguise to find out who is betraying the kingdom.

**General.** Your highness, you would never do such a thing!

**Mentuhotep.** But I would, General. And I have. (Rahotep *looks alarmed.* Nyla *enters with a goblet on a tray. She bows before* Mentuhotep.)

**Nyla.** Your drink, your highness.

**Mentuhotep.** My thirst has passed (Nyla *looks greatly relieved*), but I believe the vizier wishes to have something to drink. **8**

**Rahotep.** (*nervously*) Me, your highness? I asked for nothing—

**Mentuhotep.** But you did. Nyla, give the vizier this drink. (Nyla *moves to* Rahotep *and bows.*) It is an excellent drink, Vizier. Enjoy it.

**Rahotep.** I . . . I am not thirsty.

**Mentuhotep.** (*loudly*) Drink it!

**Rahotep.** I . . . I cannot!

**Mentuhotep.** You will do as your king commands! (Rahotep *picks up the goblet nervously.*) Now, drink!

**Rahotep.** Your highness . . .

**Mentuhotep.** Drink! (Rahotep *is about to drink when* Nyla *knocks the goblet from his hands.*)

**8 Drawing Conclusions**
Why does the Pharaoh offer the drink to Rahotep?

**Tem.** (*shocked*) Nyla!

**Rahotep.** (*hissing*) You stupid girl!

**Nyla.** (*upset*) I couldn't! I couldn't!

**Tem.** (*puzzled*) What couldn't you do?

**Mentuhotep.** Poison me or Rahotep. You did exactly as you were told, didn't you, Nyla? You put the contents of the vial into my drink.

**Nyla.** (*shocked*) How do you know this, your highness?

**Mentuhotep.** Because I told you to.

**Nyla.** (*suddenly*) Then it was you—(Mentuhotep nods.)

**Rahotep.** This girl is obviously a thief and murderer!

**Tem.** What do you mean, a thief?

**Rahotep.** She stole the golden necklace and now she's tried to kill me!

**Tem.** How do you know she stole the golden necklace?

**Rahotep.** It's all over the palace.

**Tem.** I discovered the theft only a few minutes ago. Just before you came in.

**Rahotep.** (*flustered*) But . . . but that's impossible!

**Mentuhotep.** You knew about the necklace being gone last night. It is how you blackmailed Nyla into putting the poison into the drink that was meant for me.

**General.** *(in disbelief)* Your highness! Surely the vizier was not trying to kill you!

**Mentuhotep.** But he was. He has been <u>diverting</u> gold from the treasury into his own pocket, hiding it in my mother's tomb and awaiting my death so that in the time of turmoil, he could easily <u>retrieve</u> the gold and disappear to build himself a luxurious life elsewhere.

**Rahotep.** *(sputtering)* That is absurd, your highness.

**Mentuhotep.** But you needed someone to put the poison in the goblet, someone whom you later could use as a <u>scapegoat</u> for the murder.

**Tem.** *(nodding in understanding)* Nyla. And did the necklace play a part in this?

**Nyla.** The necklace was placed in my mother's tomb. My father had made it for her.

**Mentuhotep.** So it wasn't enough to defile my mother's tomb; you also robbed this poor girl's mother's tomb.

**Rahotep.** You can't prove any of this!

**Mentuhotep.** We already have. General, take the vizier away.

**Rahotep.** You can't do this! I am the most powerful man in this palace! The guards will do as I say! They *always do* as I say!

**Mentuhotep.** And they will easily confess to helping you steal the gold. Get him out of my sight! (General *takes* Rahotep *by the arm.*)

---

**Vo•cab•u•lary**

**diverting** (duh VURT ing) causing a change in direction
**retrieve** (rih TREEV) bring back
**scapegoat** (SKAYP goht) someone who is unfairly blamed for something

**Rahotep.** *(as he's being led off right)* Nothing will come of this! You'll see! I'll escape! And I'll have the gold with me! **9** *(General and Rahotep exit.)*

**9 Visualizing**
Picture this dramatic scene.

**Tem.** Could any man but a king have as much as the vizier already has? What would make him want even more?

**Mentuhotep.** Power. He wanted to be king.

**Tem.** I guess he just wasn't smart enough.

**Nyla.** *(pulling necklace from her pocket and handing it to* Tem*)* Here is the necklace, your highness.

**Tem.** Oh, Nyla, no! It must be returned to the tomb of your mother.

**Mentuhotep.** We will see to it.

**Nyla.** *(gratefully; bowing head)* Thank you.

**Mentuhotep.** It is I who should thank you. It took courage to trust an old man hiding in the hallway of the palace.

**Nyla.** *(smiling)* He was a very wise old man, your highness. (Nyla bows, exits right as the curtain falls.) ○

## Answering the BIG Question

As you do the following activities, consider the Big Question:
**How do you keep from giving up when bad things happen?**

**WRITE TO LEARN** Think about the dilemma that Nyla faced. Write a brief entry in your Learner's Notebook describing what you would have done if you had been in her situation.

**PARTNER TALK** With a partner, discuss how Mentuhotep reacted to the bad things happening in his kingdom. How did his actions benefit him and his people?

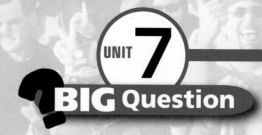

# What's worth fighting for? What's not?

*Some of the toughest decisions you make in your life will be about whether to stand up for what you believe or whether to give way. In this unit, you will read about ideas and issues that are worth fighting for. And you will encounter people who have had to confront the question: **What's worth fighting for? What's not?***

## Key Reading Skills

As you read the selections in this unit, apply these reading skills.

- **Distinguishing Fact from Opinion** Ask yourself if a statement can be proved with supporting information. If so, it's a fact. If not, it's an opinion—a statement of someone's personal viewpoint.
- **Questioning** Check your understanding by asking yourself questions as you read. Also ask yourself what information in a selection is important and why.
- **Clarifying** Pause after a difficult section of a selection and clear up any doubts you might have about its meaning.
- **Reviewing** Go back over what you have read to find important information and to organize it in your mind.

# Jackie Robinson, Baseball's Pathfinder

by Ruth Dorfman

**Find out just how much courage it took to be the first African-American player in the major leagues.**

ow would Derek Jeter of the New York Yankees feel if he stepped back in time to the early 1940s? Very strange. The first thing he would have to do would be to change his <u>occupation</u>!

## Vo•cab•u•lary

**occupation** (ah kyoo PAY shun) job; profession

Fifty-five years ago only white players were hired by major league baseball teams. Black men could only play on all-black minor league teams. Baseball was a <u>segregated</u> sport. ❶

Grandson of a slave, son of a <u>sharecropper</u>, Jackie Robinson was one of five children his mother had to support when Jackie's father deserted her. Wanting the best possible future for her family, Mallie Robinson took her children and headed for Pasadena, California, where her brother lived.

❶ **Questioning**
Why is this information so important to understanding this selection?

As early as third grade, Jackie's outstanding athletic ability was noticed. By then, every kid in his elementary school who played sports knew the answers to the questions: Who can get the most hits? Who can score the most points? Even the youngest players in the schoolyard knew that to have Jackie on your team meant one thing: winning!

Besides his mother, who taught him the importance of a close-knit family, Jackie was influenced by two other people growing up. They were Carl Anderson and Reverend Karl Downs. Anderson was a mechanic who had a repair shop on the street where Jackie lived. The black, Japanese, and Mexican kids in Jackie's neighborhood formed street gangs to feel they were part of a group. Anderson noticed Jackie's involvement with a neighborhood gang and advised Jackie to leave them. "True courage doesn't mean following the crowd. It's doing the right thing even if you have to do it alone." Jackie was never sorry for following that advice.

Reverend Karl Downs, pastor of the church where the Robinsons worshiped, also helped Jackie break away from the street gangs. Realizing that the church had to provide activities for young members as options to hanging out on the streets, the young

## Vo·cab·u·lary

**segregated** (SEH gruh gay tud) separated according to skin color
**sharecropper** (SHAYR krah pur) a farmer who rents his or her fields from an owner and pays the owner with part of the crop

minister went into action. He scheduled dances at the church and installed a badminton court. While loudly criticized for some of these changes, Reverend Downs didn't back down. His <u>courteous</u> attitude left a lasting impression on Jackie.

Jackie's athletic ability improved as he got older. In high school, he earned letters in football, baseball, basketball, and track. Later, playing first-string quarterback at Pasadena Junior College, Jackie helped Pasadena win all eleven football games in one season! While at Pasadena, Jackie set a new broad jump record of twenty-five feet six and a half inches, beating the record that had been set by his brother Mack. Mack was also a champion sprinter, having finished second to gold medalist Jesse Owens in the 1936 Olympics.

Gaining <u>publicity</u> from his athletic feats, Jackie received many offers of athletic scholarships. He chose UCLA because it was close to home. There, he became the university's first four-letter man. A star player without a star's <u>temperament</u>, Jackie was always a team player first. He never risked his team's chances by grabbing the spotlight for himself. ❷ Unconvinced that a college education could help a black man get a job, Robinson left UCLA after two years. Wanting to help youngsters, he was lucky to get a job as assistant athletic director in a camp for kids from poor or broken homes. However, the job didn't last long because World War II broke out.

> ❷ **Clarifying**
> List the qualities that made Jackie Robinson such a valuable player.

After serving in the army, Jackie got a job with the Kansas City Monarchs, a black professional baseball team. In those days,

## Vo·cab·u·lary

**courteous** (KUR tee us) polite
**publicity** (puh BLIH sih tee) public attention
**temperament** (TEMP ruh ment) personality

blacks could only play on black teams, and their living conditions were very hard. For example, in the South, even small-town coffee shops would permit blacks to only take out food, and hotel accommodations for people of color were practically nonexistent. Sometimes, they would be lucky to land in a town where black families would take in as many players as they could. Mostly, though, they had to spend their nights sleeping on the bus.

A white man could have carved out a career in baseball in 1944, but it seemed to hold no future for a black man. The black press, some politicians, and sportswriters were fighting to break down the Jim Crow barriers, but it didn't seem to Jackie that it would happen in his lifetime.

Little did he know that Branch Rickey, the president of the Brooklyn Dodgers, was planning to challenge baseball as an all-white sport. A courageous man who felt that Jim Crow baseball was morally wrong, Rickey also felt that black players in the major leagues would bring more black fans to the games.

And so he persuaded the Brooklyn Dodgers' directors to let their club be the pioneer in bringing blacks into big-time baseball. Rickey's "noble experiment" involved finding an ideal black player who, running the gauntlet toward public acceptance, would open the doors for other black players. Such a player had to have unique qualities. He had to be able to take verbal and physical abuse and not fight back. He had to do this without bitterness in order to win acceptance. He would have to cast off his attitude of humbleness and act like a winner. But a winner without bitterness. "Mr. Rickey," Robinson asked, "are you looking for a Negro who is afraid to fight back?"

## Vo·cab·u·lary

**press** (prehs) newspapers and magazines
**Jim Crow** (jim croh) name for laws that made segregation legal
**running the gauntlet** (RUN ing the GAWNT lut) going through a long, difficult time

Rickey exploded. "Robinson, I'm looking for a ballplayer with guts enough not to fight back!" Thereupon, he launched into a lecture on what Jackie might have to face, including taunts about his race and his family in almost <u>unendurable</u> language. Rickey pointed out that some <u>bigots</u> might try to provoke a race riot at the game. It would be their way of proving to the public what happens when you let a black man into the major leagues.

While it seemed an almost unbearable sacrifice that was being asked of him, Jackie knew that he had to make it. He had to be the one to suffer humiliation and worse, so that black youngsters might have a future.

However, some of his Dodger teammates didn't want Robinson to have a future. A group of them secretly agreed to sign a petition stating that they would not play with him on the team.

Luckily, Rickey found out about the plot. "Anyone not willing to have a black teammate can quit!" he warned. No one left.

But Jackie's greatest test of enduring racial insults without striking back was ahead of him. Walking to the plate at the start of a three-game series against the Philadelphia Phillies, he could hardly believe the insults he heard coming from the Phillies' dugout.

"Why don't you go back to the cotton fields where you belong?"

"They're waiting for you in the jungles, black boy!"

Though the Phillies were a northern team, their manager, Ben Chapman, was a Southerner. It was Chapman who directed this stream of hatred at Jackie. Loyal to his agreement with Rickey, Jackie had to hold his tongue

## Vo•cab•u•lary

**unendurable** (un in DUR uh bul) unbearable; too painful to tolerate
**bigots** (BIG uts) people who hate people of other races

until he was saved by his own teammates.

*Jackie Robinson with Branch Rickey, Sr.*

Outraged by the behavior of the players from the City of Brotherly Love, Ed Stanky, a white teammate of Jackie's, yelled back, "Listen, you yellow-bellied cowards. Why don't you yell at somebody who can answer back?"

In later years, Rickey said, "Chapman did more than anybody to unite the Dodgers. When he poured out that string of abuse, he unified thirty men. Chapman made Jackie a real member of the Dodgers."

In 1962, five years after he had retired from baseball, Jackie Robinson was inducted into baseball's Hall of Fame. At this ceremony, Jackie paid tribute to Branch Rickey, saying, "He was as a father to me." **3**

**3 Reviewing**
Make a list of the people who influenced Jackie Robinson and how they did it.

While creating a path for future baseball players of color, Jackie Robinson won the respect and admiration of fans and players regardless of race. He proved that it was a person's character and ability that counted, not the color of his skin. ○

## Answering the BIG Question

As you do the following activities, consider the Big Question:
**What's worth fighting for? What's not?**

**WRITE TO LEARN** Put yourself in Jackie Robinson's shoes. Write an entry in your Learner's Notebook about how he must have felt when he came up to bat against the Philadelphia Phillies.

**LITERATURE GROUPS** Join with two or three other students who have read this selection. Discuss the sacrifices that Jackie Robinson made to pave the way for other African-American players.

# For my 'Pen Pal' in Louisiana:

# Video asks about life after Katrina

by Kery Murakami

---

**Teens reach out across the country to kids whose lives have been turned upside-down.**

---

J illian Rood, the woman behind the video camera, called out: "Quiet on the set."

The set was a meeting room at Delridge Community Center in West Seattle, where five boys took turns sitting on a couch in front of the camera.

"I feel sorry for people in Louisiana, because when we had an earthquake in Seattle, I was really scared. I know in Louisiana it was really hard because everything went away because of the hurricane," Mark Green, 13, said into the camera.

Sometime next month, youths <u>evacuated</u> from New Orleans because of Hurricane Katrina will be looking at the videotape at the A.C. Lewis YMCA in Baton Rouge, La. They'll make their own videotape, talking about their lives and answering questions posed by the Seattle youths in a tape they'll send back. Then the Seattle kids will answer with another videotape and so on.

"It's sort of like video pen pals," said Susan Malmquist, who works with teens at the community center.

"This was the beginning," said Rood, who runs youth programs for Seattle's public access television station, the Seattle Community Access Network. She and Malmquist came up with the idea because they wanted youths here to feel a connection with the young victims of the hurricane.

So often, Rood said, the <u>barrage</u> of <u>devastation</u> that comes through television can be <u>numbing</u>, like something out of a movie. ❶ By exchanging videotapes, she said she wanted the youths at the community center to know there were real people in the images.

> ❶ **Clarifying**
> What point is Rood making here?

In Baton Rouge, Monice Oliphant, who works with teens at the YMCA, said she wanted the youths there to know real people were concerned about them.

## Vo•cab•u•lary

**evacuated** (ih VAK yoo ayt ud) left an area because of danger
**barrage** (buh RAWZH) an attack; a high volume of things, ideas, or images coming all at once
**devastation** (dev uh STAY shun) total destruction
**numbing** (NUM ing) having the ability to make a person numb or unfeeling

The real people here include Green, in a silver basketball jersey with Iverson on it, a do-rag and a visor cocked sideways, who said: "I am 13 years old and I grew up in Seattle. My favorite sport is basketball. My favorite color is blue. I like gumbo, Louisiana-style. Yup."

The youths in Baton Rouge will hear from D'Nique Harris-Welch, who said at Friday's taping that he is 13, and likes baseball, basketball and football. Off-camera, he said making the video was like the movie "Pay It Forward" because he didn't want anything in return, but maybe the people in Louisiana would see the concern and help someone else in turn.

Rood said the idea has <u>spawned</u> others, such as a project she's working on with Ethiopian youths growing up in Seattle.

They'll make their own videotape asking youths in Ethiopia what it's like growing up there.

On Friday, there were several takes. Travis Madison, 13, started giggling. Darvell Maund, 13, looked into the camera, staring open-mouthed. Words escaped him.

"I can't go first," he said. "I froze."

Then Maund asked, "What experiences would you like to share with other kids?"

Harris-Welch asked, "Are you able to go to school or are you not?"

"The other thing I wanted to know was, did the news show what it was really like?" he said.

Madison asked, "How old are you?"

Jahmel Hayes, who wore a black Delridge Community Council Track T-shirt, asked, "How has the hurricane changed your lives?"

And Green added, "Has there been anything positive about it?"

Now, they're waiting for the answers. ○

---

## Answering the BIG Question

As you do the following activities, consider the Big Question:
**What's worth fighting for? What's not?**

**WRITE TO LEARN** What questions would you like to ask survivors of a hurricane or other natural disasters? Write them in your Learner's Notebook.

**PARTNER TALK** Think of a natural disaster that has happened recently. Meet with a partner to discuss what you could do to reach out to teens affected by this disaster.

---

## Vo•cab•u•lary

**spawned** (spawnd) gave birth to; started

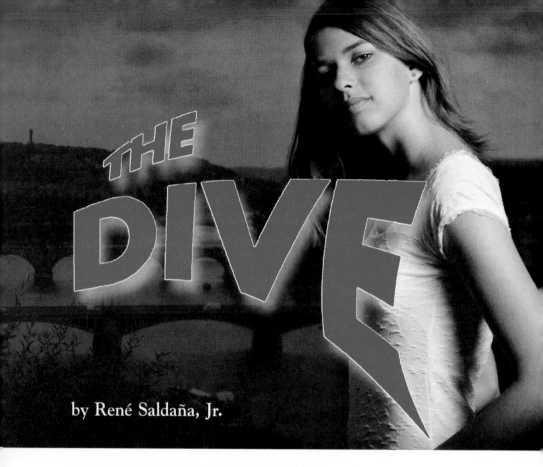

# THE DIVE

by René Saldaña, Jr.

---

**What does it take to prove your adulthood?**

---

"**L**ook at them, Papi," said Melly to her father.

Mr. Otero cast his line into the water again and looked up and to his right. *"Tan locos, mi'ja.* It's a crazy thing to do."

From upriver, Melly and her father could see five or six boys fixing to jump from Jensen's Bridge. They pounded their chests, inched their way to the edge, then dove in all at once, some headfirst, others feet first, and one balled up. The boys disappeared underwater, leaving behind them different sized splashes, then Melly heard the echoes of their jumping screams a full second or two after they'd gone under. By then, they were shooting up out of the water, their arms raised in the air. They'd done it. Most of the boys in Three Oaks had to dive from the bridge at one time or other to prove themselves real men. Today was their day.

Melly saw the boys crawl from the river and turn over on their backs, stretched out like lizards sunning themselves on the bank. Reeling in her line, she thought, So what if they can dive off the bridge! I could do it too if I wanted. Who said it was just for the guys to do?

"You'll do nothing of the kind," said Mr. Otero.

"Huh?"

"You said you could dive too if you wanted?"

"I didn't say anything. You must be hearing things."

He smiled. "Just like your mother. Talking your thoughts aloud." ❶ He reached over and touched his rough hand to her cheek.

> ❶ **Clarifying**
> How does Melly's father know what she is thinking?

Melly blushed. She stood and set her rod on a rock, then stretched. She held her face and wondered if it was red from the sun. Red from her father's touch?

All along she'd actually been talking. She'd heard the same thing from her _tías_, from Mama Tochi, and from her sister, Becky. "Your mom literally spoke her mind," the aunts all told her.

"You're so much like your mother," Mr. Otero told her, casting again.

"She probably would've jumped," she said.

"Probably so, but I said you won't do it. _M'entiendes?_"

"Yes, sir, I understand. No jumping from the bridge." She looked downriver, then set her sight on the bridge. Her face was warm, as she imagined her mother jumping from the bridge, her long black hair in a ponytail, or all loose and curly; her mother slicing into the water, then exploding out, all smiles and laughter. Beautiful.

---

## Vo•cab•u•lary

**tías** (TEE ahs) aunts (Spanish)

"What?"

"What what?"

"Never mind. Just like your mother."

That evening, Melly went to visit her grandmother, Mama Tochi, down the street from where Melly lived with her father and her sister, who'd only recently left for college.

Mama Tochi had lived on her own ever since Melly's grandfather died five years ago. When Mama Tochi's children all moved and married, each begged her to come live with them, but she refused. She said, "For decades I took care of both your father and myself when you left the house for work and school, and before that I took care of six of you, from dirty diapers to broken hearts, so what makes you think I need to be looked after?"

Mr. Otero, Melly's dad, was the only one to pull up stakes and move to be closer to Mama Tochi when Papa 'Tero died. Moving was easy for him. His own wife had died a year before his father's passing, and he once confessed to Mama Tochi, "With Aurelia gone, I don't know that I can do right by our two girls." **2**

Melly knocked at her grandmother's and walked in. It was early evening, so she knew that Mama Tochi would be out in her backyard garden with her babies: the herbs that ran up along the house; then the *rosales*, four bushes of them, red, yellow, white, and pink, big as trees almost; countless wildflower patches; and Melly's favorite, the esperanza bushes, the yellow bells soft on her cheeks. The backyard smelled like honey tasted.

**2 Reviewing**
Look back through the paragraphs you've already read and make a mental map of Melly's family.

She went out the screen door and said, "Mama Tochi. Where are you?" Melly could hear the water splashing, but couldn't quite make out her grandmother.

---

### Vo•cab•u•lary

**rosales** (ro SAH lays) rosebushes (Spanish)

"*Aqui, mi'jita*. I'm over here." Mama Tochi was hidden behind the esperanza bush, watering it with her pail. She'd set the hose at the base of one of the rosales. "You don't even have to tell me why you're here. You want to jump from that crazy bridge."

Sometimes Melly thought her grandmother could read minds, see into the future, even talk to the dead. Melly couldn't figure out why she came over for advice. She never got anything but *cuentos* from Mama Tochi, stories that somehow served as life lessons. That time Melly had had the chance to cheat on her end-of-term exam her ninth-grade year, Mama Tochi said, "I remember a time I was calling bingo. Playing that night was my worst enemy, Perla. I kept an eye all night on her four cards, praying a secret prayer that she'd lose every time. On one of her cards I could see all she needed was El Gallo. Without knowing why, I pulled a card from the middle of the deck instead of the top. I pulled La Chalupa, and Manuela won. I was afraid to look at the top card. I collected all the others and shuffled them real fast. What if it had been El Gallo? I wasn't able to look in Perla's eyes for two weeks and a half, that's how guilty I felt."

Lessons to be learned that time? You do it, you'll get caught. You'll feel worse if you don't get caught.

"It won't be cheating, really, Mama Tochi. The teacher's already said chances of me passing are slim. There's stuff on the test we've never studied even."

Mama Tochi sat on the porch swing and said, "You're a big girl. You'll know what to do."

That night, Melly considered what her grandmother had said. She saw herself three years later, marching for graduation, everyone taking photos, everyone smiling, everyone happy, except she wouldn't be because she'd remember having cheated that time back in the ninth grade. She didn't sleep at all that night. The next day, even before the exam was handed out, two boys and one girl were called out of class. Earlier in the week, they had asked

---

## Vo•cab•u•lary

**mi'jita** (mee HEE tah) contraction of **mi hijita**, my little girl (Spanish)

Melly if she wanted a look at the test. They'd found it in one of the teacher's desks and ran off a copy. The morning of the test, she told them, "No thanks. I'll just try my best. I'll fail on my own terms, you know." **3** Then they got busted, and Melly passed the test by two points. "A pass is a pass," said Mama Tochi. That's just what Melly's mom used to say.

**3 Clarifying**
Why did Melly decide not to cheat?

Tonight, Melly said, "What d'you mean? I'm here to visit my favorite Mama Tochi."

"Don't give me that. Your papi's already called. He's worried you're gonna jump and get tangled up in the weeds at the bottom of the river and drown."

Melly said, "Ah, Papi knows there's no weeds down there. And besides, no one's ever drowned at the bridge before."

Mama Tochi put down the pail, turned off the hose, then said, "Sit down. I'll bring coffee."

Melly sat under the orange tree. Papa 'Tero had built the table and chairs years ago. He also had carved each of his children's and grandchildren's names and dates of birth into the tabletop in a great big circle. At the center were his name and Mama Tochi's. Servando Otero and Rosario Garcia de Otero, their dates of birth, and the date of their wedding. Melly traced mama Tochi's name.

"I put two spoons of sugar and a little milk in yours, just like you drink it," said Mama Tochi.

"*Gracias,*" said Melly. "It's not that high of a jump—ten, fifteen feet at most."

"That's not high. About two of my rosebushes, right." Mama Tochi looked up where the top of the invisible bush would be.

"I mean, if the guys can do it—Aren't you the one always saying, 'You can do anything and everything you set your heart to'?"

"You're right, *mi'jita.* Anything is possible. How's your coffee?"

"Good, thank you, Mama Tochi."

"*Mi'jita,* have I ever told you that my mother never let me drink coffee? It was a grown-up thing to do. I didn't take my first drink of it until I was twenty-one."

Melly knew there was a reason Mama Tochi was telling her this. She just had to figure it out. She had to pay attention, then sleep on it, and if she hadn't figured it out by after school tomorrow, she'd have to come visit a second time, get another story, then try to figure out two lessons instead of one.

"I'd gotten my first job as a <u>seamstress</u>," Mama Tochi continued. "'My first paycheck,' I told my mother, 'First thing I'll buy is a cup of coffee at Martins Café.' My mother said, 'Then you'll buy for us all.' And so I did, a cup of coffee and a piece of sweet bread for everyone, all thirteen of us. I spent every peso I'd made, and I didn't sleep all night. But I loved the taste so much I haven't stopped, even when Dr. Neely told me I should. What does he know?"

She sat across the table from Melly and sipped her coffee.

Melly thought she'd figured out the lesson: that she should dive, and then she wouldn't be able to stop. She'd be as old as Mama Tochi and diving would still be in her blood, and one day

## Vo•cab•u•lary

**seamstress** (SEEM strus) a woman who sews and alters clothing for a living

she'd jump from a bridge too high for such a <u>frail</u> woman and break every bone in her body and drown. But she'd be doing what she loved.

"This is some good coffee," Mama Tochi said.

"Sure is. Good bread, too."

"Twenty-one, can you believe it? Today you kids have all these fancy cafés in your fancy bookstores where you go and study with all your friends. What was that drink you brought me once? Iced café mocha? Why ruin a good cup of coffee with chocolate syrup? Why ruin it by pouring it into a paper cup? Not like in the old days. A little crema, a pinch of sugar, and steaming hot in a clay jar."

It only seemed like Mama Tochi had finished telling her story. Melly knew better, so she leaned back, ready for more. She knew she hadn't figured out her grandmother's riddle yet.

"Nowadays, you babies grow up too fast. You're women before you're girls. You never get to be girls, some of you. It's not a bad thing, the way the world is today. You have to know more sooner, and be able to survive it. In my day, all I had to worry about was drinking my first cup of coffee, my first job, and hoping my family would choose the right man for me. They did that back then, you know, chose your husband. My father tried to find the man for me, and—well, let's just say, I was ahead of my time when I told my father I would not marry Marcos Antonio Velasquez. Papa told me, '<u>¿Y tú, quién te crees?</u>' I was twenty-three then, and getting too old to be playing this game, my father said. But I— I had to take a stand sometime. After all," she said, and laughed. Melly imagined Mama Tochi's young face laughing, her wrinkles somehow gone. "After all, I was a woman now. I was drinking coffee at Martin's every Friday afternoon on my way home. But I didn't smoke like some of the others. I tried that once, but once was all I needed. I didn't like the taste. Coffee, now there's taste.

## Vo•cab•u•lary

**frail** (frail) delicate; fragile
**¿Y tú, quién te crees?** (ee TU, kyen tay crais) And you, who do you think you are? (Spanish)

Tobacco? Take it or leave it. Better leave it." She sipped some more, then said, "*Mi'jita,* it's getting late. You better go home before your papi calls looking for you."

Melly stood and helped her with the cups and plate of bread. She hooked the screen door shut. She didn't close the inside door. Mama Tochi always said she wanted to smell the flowers. "And what's there in this house to steal? I wish someone would come and take that television. It's just something else I have to dust." Melly knew Mama Tochi was teasing. She liked to watch her Mexican soaps.

"Dive if you want, *mi'jita.* I know you can make it. You won't drown. You're strong like all those boys, and smarter. So if you feel you have to, then go ahead, jump from the bridge. It'll make you feel better. " **4**

**4 Questioning**
What advice does Melly's grandmother give her?

Melly hugged her grandmother tight, then said, "*Buenas noches,* Mama Tochi."

"*Buenas.*"

Melly was happy. She'd gotten her grandmother's permission. Now her father couldn't say anything about it.

Melly woke to someone revving a car engine down the street. She'd gone to sleep thinking about her grandmother standing up to her own father, looking him in the eye: "I will not marry that boy. I don't love him." Melly imagined her great-grandfather stomping his foot, crinkling his face, pointing at his daughter, and not able to say a word to her. That's how angry Melly imagined him to be, so angry he was speechless. Then later, as the young Mama Tochi was falling asleep, Melly pictured her great-grandfather bursting into the bedroom to say, "No daughter of mine—I shouldn't have let you drink coffee." And that would be it. He'd slam the door shut, and Rosario wouldn't have to marry Marcos Antonio Velasquez.

Instead she married Servando Otero, a handsome man till the end of his days. Melly remembered how his unshaven face had scratched at her cheeks when he held her tight to him. Like her own father's face tickled her cheeks now when he didn't shave on weekends. Earlier, at the river, she had noticed more gray in her father's stubble. She'd reached over and rubbed his face. He'd touched her cheek. She laughed and said, "I hope my face isn't as hard as yours."

He shook his head. "Not in a million years. Your face is like your mom's. Soft. Very much a woman's face."

Melly caressed her cheek. Like mom, she thought.

"Yep, so much like her. Don't get me wrong. You're hard as nails inside. Tough, and thick-headed, too." He cast his rod again and said, "Just like your mom."

That's when she saw the boys jumping.

In bed, she felt her cheek where her father had touched it. She knew she wouldn't jump. She didn't have to. She was already grown. Had a woman's face. Had nothing to prove to anybody. Tomorrow, if she wanted to, she could tell her father, "I'm diving no matter what you say." But she wouldn't. She was already drinking coffee, like her Mama Tochi. **5**

Melly turned onto her side. The window was open, and a cool breeze blew in. Melly could smell the sweetness of the flowers and herbs wafting from across the street. She smiled, closed her eyes, and slept. ○

**5 Reviewing**
Go back through the story and list the steps that lead up to Melly's decision.

---

## Answering the BIG Question

As you do the following activities, consider the Big Question:
**What's worth fighting for? What's not?**

**WRITE TO LEARN** Think about who you turn to when you need advice. In your Learner's Notebook describe the qualities this person has that make him or her a good adviser.

**PARTNER TALK** Mama Tochi describes the conversation she and her father had when she refused to marry Marcos Antonio Velasquez. Role-play that conversation with a partner.

# Sleepless

## at Sea

by Naila Moreira

---

**How much sleep does a baby orca-whale need?**

---

*W*ouldn't it be great to stay up all night without feeling tired the next day?

Orca-whale and dolphin babies and moms are champions of sleeplessness. They stay awake for a month after the babies are born—without showing any ill effects. And they don't even need extra sleep later on to make up for the loss.

Oleg Lyamin of the University of California, Los Angeles studies marine <u>mammals</u> such as orcas and dolphins. He discovered these animals' unusual sleep habits by watching orca Kasatka and her baby Nakai at SeaWorld, San Diego, just after Nakai was born.

---

## Vo•cab•u•lary

**mammals** (MAM ulz) animals that give birth to live young

## Sleepless at Sea

Kasatka and Nakai swam around their pool 24 hours a day, instead of floating motionless and closing their eyes the way that other adult orcas do when they sleep. Adults typically sleep for 5 to 8 hours. ❶

Lyamin and his fellow researchers visited dolphin moms and babies at the Utrish Dolphinarium in Russia to see if they did the same thing. Dolphins are strange sleepers to begin with. A dolphin snoozes with only one-half of its brain at a time, closing one eye and either floating or swimming. But mother and newborn dolphins didn't even sleep that much. Instead, they kept both eyes open and swam around constantly.

❶ **Distinguishing Fact from Opinion** Are the statements in this paragraph facts or opinions? Explain.

No other mammal has ever been found to sleep so little for so long. Moreover, most mammal babies, including those of humans, typically need much more sleep than adults do. In contrast, Nakai and the dolphin infants needed even less sleep than their moms.

Both mother and baby whales and dolphins <u>gradually</u> increased their sleep to normal adult levels over a period of months.

Scientists who study sleep are surprised by the findings. Other animals, such as rats, get sick or die if they're deprived of sleep. Many researchers have argued that people and animals need sleep in order to learn, just as students in school need a good night's rest after studying to do well on an exam. Babies in particular need sleep so that their brains can develop.

Both orcas and dolphins are intelligent animals with large brains. Because orca and dolphin babies don't seem to doze at all while their brains are growing, they must not need sleep for learning or brain development, argues Jerry Siegel, who worked with Lyamin. He suggests that sleep serves other, as yet unknown, roles in mammals.

---

## Vo•cab•u•lary

**gradually** (GRAD joo uhl ee) slowly; over a period of time

It's also possible that orcas and dolphins have <u>evolved</u> special ways to develop and learn without sleep. Or, these marine mammals may simply have an unusual form of "sleep-swimming." It'd be like a sleepwalker who goes to the kitchen, opens the refrigerator, and grabs a snack while brainwave recordings would show he or she is in a deep sleep.

Why do orcas and dolphins need to remain constantly active after a baby is born? Maybe they need to stay active to survive, Siegel says.

First, newborns need to breathe every 30 seconds, and mothers help push their babies to the surface to breathe, Siegel says. Secondly, baby whales and dolphins haven't yet developed the thick <u>blubber</u> coat that protects them against the cold ocean waters when they're older. Staying active may help keep them warm.

Don't try to copy the sleeping feats of orcas and dolphins at home, researchers warn. Scientists may someday learn how to help people <u>skimp</u> on sleep. For now, though, people still have to snooze at least 8 hours a night to stay healthy. ○

## Answering the BIG Question

As you do the following activities, consider the Big Question:
**What's worth fighting for? What's not?**

**WRITE TO LEARN** Do you think these baby animals and their mothers need to stay awake so the babies can survive? Why or why not? Write your answer in your Learner's Notebook.

**PARTNER TALK** Meet with a partner who has read "Sleepless at Sea." Talk about what it might be like to stay awake for a month. What would you do with your extra waking hours?

## Vo•cab•u•lary

**evolved** (ih VAHLVD) developed
**blubber** (BLUB ur) layer of fat under the skin of sea mammals
**skimp** (skimp) use a too-small amount of something

# Sleeping Soundly for a *Longer Life*

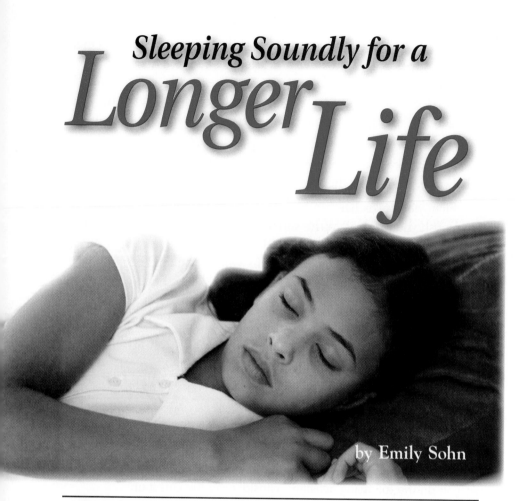

by Emily Sohn

**Follow the advice in this article, and you may be able to add years to your life.**

Y ou've heard it before: If you know what's good for you, you'll go to bed on time. Now, scientists are saying something more about going to sleep. And you may lose more than just TV privileges if you don't listen. You might end up shaving years off your life.

For 19 years, psychologist Mary A. Dew of the University of Pittsburgh School of Medicine and her colleagues tracked 186 healthy elderly adults, who were mostly between 60 and 80 years old. Part of the research involved monitoring brain waves of the people as they slept.

At the end of the study, the people who had trouble falling or staying asleep were more likely to die sooner from natural causes compared to those who slept well, the researchers reported.

# *more sleep = longer life*

Scientists aren't yet sure why losing sleep might shorten lives. Some experts think sleep <u>deprivation</u> weakens the immune system, making it harder to fight off illnesses. Other studies have linked sleep <u>disorders</u> to heart and brain diseases. **❶**

❶ **Clarifying**
What did Mary A. Dew's study show? What might explain the results?

The new study focused on older people. But there may be a lesson here for all of us: Work hard, play hard, sleep well. You just might wake up to a longer future. ○

---

## Answering the BIG Question

As you do the following activities, consider the Big Question:
**What's worth fighting for? What's not?**

**WRITE TO LEARN** Think about how you feel after a good night's sleep. Then think about how you feel after a bad night's sleep. How does the quality of your sleep affect you? Record your thoughts in your Learner's Notebook.

**LITERATURE GROUPS** Join with two or three other students who have read this selection. Discuss whether you sometimes have trouble making time for a full night's sleep. Talk about ways you could make more time for sleep.

---

## Vo•cab•u•lary

**deprivation** (de pruh VAY shun) lack
**disorders** (dis OR durz) diseases; problems

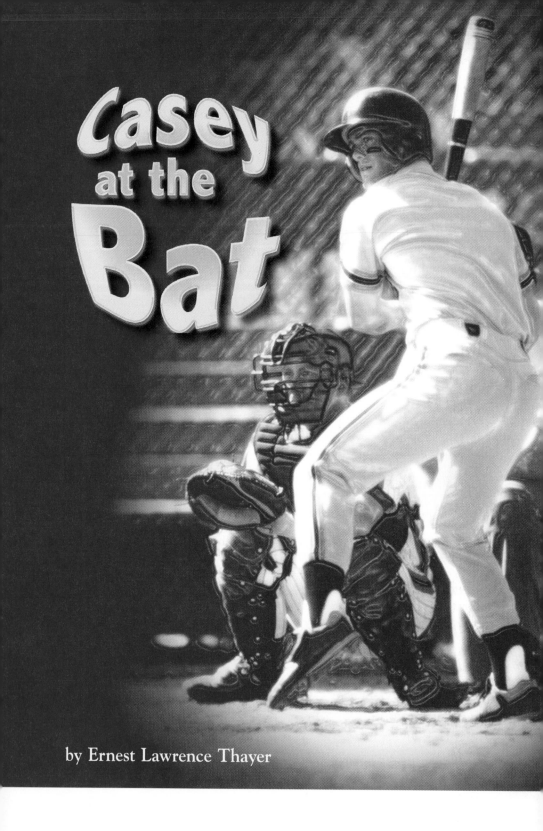

# Casey at the Bat

by Ernest Lawrence Thayer

The outlook wasn't brilliant
for the Mudville nine that day:
The score stood four to two
with but one inning more to play.

And then when Cooney died at first,
and Barrows did the same,
A sickly silence fell
upon the patrons of the game.

A straggling few got up
to go in deep despair. The rest
Clung to that hope which springs eternal
in the human breast;

They thought if only Casey
could but get a whack at that—
We'd put up even money now
with Casey at the bat.

But Flynn preceded Casey,
as did also Jimmy Blake,
And the former was a <u>lulu</u>
and the latter was a <u>cake</u>;

So upon that <u>stricken</u> multitude
grim <u>melancholy</u> sat,
For there seemed but little chance
of Casey's getting to that bat.

## Vo•cab•u•lary

**lulu** (LOO loo) someone who stands out for being extremely good or extremely bad at something
**cake** (kayk) easy to strike out
**stricken** (STRIK un) shocked
**melancholy** (MEL un kaw lee) sad

But Flynn let drive a single,
to the wonderment of all,
And Blake, the much despis-ed,
tore the cover off the ball;

And when the dust had lifted,
and the men saw what had occurred,
There was Jimmy safe at second
and Flynn a-hugging third.

Then from 5,000 throats and more
there rose a <u>lusty</u> yell;
It rumbled through the valley,
it rattled in the <u>dell</u>;

It knocked upon the mountain
and <u>recoiled</u> upon the flat,
For Casey, mighty Casey,
was advancing to the bat. ❶

**❶ Reviewing**
What's the status of the game when Casey comes up to bat?

There was ease in Casey's manner
as he stepped into his place;
There was pride in Casey's bearing
and a smile on Casey's face.

And when, responding to the cheers,
he lightly <u>doffed</u> his hat,
No stranger in the crowd could doubt
'twas Casey at the bat.

## Vo•cab•u•lary

**lusty** (LUST ee) vigorous; enthusiastic
**dell** (del) valley
**recoiled** (rih KOYLD) bounced back
**doffed** (dawft) raised in salute

Ten thousand eyes were on him
as he rubbed his hands with dirt;
Five thousand tongues applauded him
when he wiped them on his shirt.

Then while the <u>writhing</u> pitcher
ground the ball into his hip,
Defiance gleamed in Casey's eye,
a sneer curled Casey's lip.

And now the leather-covered sphere
came hurtling through the air,
And Casey stood a-watching it
in <u>haughty</u> <u>grandeur</u> there.

Close by the sturdy batsman
the ball <u>unheeded</u> sped—
"This ain't my style," said Casey.
"Strike one," the umpire said.

From the benches, black with people,
there went up a muffled roar,
Like the beating of the storm-waves
on a stern and distant shore.

"Kill him! Kill the umpire!"
shouted someone on the stand;
And it's likely they'd have killed him
had not Casey raised his hand.

## Vo•cab•u•lary

**writhing** (RY thing) squirming
**haughty** (HAW tee) arrogant; snobbish
**grandeur** (GRAN jur) magnificence
**unheeded** (un HEED ud) unnoticed

With a smile of Christian charity
great Casey's <u>visage</u> shone;
He stilled the rising <u>tumult</u>;
he bade the game go on;

He signaled to the pitcher,
and once more the spheroid flew;
But Casey still ignored it,
and the umpire said, "Strike two."

"Fraud!" cried the maddened thousands,
and the echo answered fraud;
But one scornful look from Casey
and the audience was awed.

---

## Vo·cab·u·lary
**visage** (VIZ uj) face
**tumult** (TOO mult) confused noise

They saw his face grow stern and cold,
they saw his muscles strain,
And they knew that Casey
wouldn't let that ball go by again.

The sneer is gone from Casey's lips,
his teeth are clenched in hate;
He pounds with cruel violence
his bat upon the plate. ❷

❷ **Clarifying**
What must
Casey do now?

And now the pitcher holds the ball,
and now he lets it go,
And now the air is shattered
by the force of Casey's blow.

Oh, somewhere in this favored land
the sun is shining bright;
The band is playing somewhere,
and somewhere hearts are light,

And somewhere men are laughing,
and somewhere children shout;
But there is no joy in Mudville—
mighty Casey has struck out. ○

## Answering the BIG Question

As you do the following activities, consider the Big Question:
**What's worth fighting for? What's not?**

**WRITE TO LEARN** Put yourself in Casey's shoes. How do you think he felt after he struck out? How do you think he behaved on the field? Answer these questions in a brief entry in your Learner's Notebook.

**LITERATURE GROUPS** Get together with two or three other students who have read "Casey at the Bat." Discuss dramatic moments in games in which you were a spectator or a player.

from

# A Single Shard

### by Linda Sue Park

---

**How can a hungry boy fill his stomach without harming his soul?**

---

"Eh, Tree-ear! Have you hungered well today?" Crane-man called out as Tree-ear drew near the bridge.

The well-fed of the village greeted each other politely by saying, "Have you eaten well today?" Tree-ear and his friend turned the greeting inside out for their own little joke.

Tree-ear squeezed the bulging pouch that he wore at his waist. He had meant to hold back the good news, but the excitement spilled out of him. "Crane-man! A good thing that you greeted me so just now, for later today we will have to use the proper words!" He held the bag high. Tree-ear was delighted when Crane-man's eyes widened in surprise. He knew that Crane-man would guess at once—only one thing could give a bag that kind of smooth fullness. Not carrot tops or chicken bones, which <u>protruded</u> in odd lumps. No, the bag was filled with *rice*.

Crane-man raised his walking crutch in a salute. "Come, my young friend! Tell me how you came by such a fortune—a tale worth hearing, no doubt!" **1**

Tree-ear had been trotting along the road on his early-morning <u>perusal</u> of the village <u>rubbish</u> heaps. Ahead of him a man carried a heavy load on a *jiggeh*, an open-framed backpack made of branches. On the *jiggeh* was a large woven-straw container, the kind commonly used to carry rice.

**1 Clarifying**
What is the "fortune" that Crane-man is talking about?

Tree-ear knew that the rice must be from last year's crop; in the fields surrounding the village this season's rice had only just begun to grow. It would be many months before the rice was harvested and the poor allowed to <u>glean</u> the fallen grain from the bare fields. Only then would they taste the pure flavor of rice and feel its solid goodness in their bellies. Just looking at the straw box made water rush into Tree-ear's mouth.

The man had paused in the road and hoisted the wooden *jiggeh* higher on his back, shifting the <u>cumbersome</u> weight. As

## Vo•cab•u•lary
**protruded** (pruh TROOD ud) stuck out
**perusal** (puh ROOZ uhl) the act of searching through something
**rubbish** (RUB bish) garbage
**glean** (gleen) pick up the grains that remain in a field after the crop has been harvested
**cumbersome** (KUM bur sum) awkward; heavy

Tree-ear stared, rice began to trickle out of a hole in the straw box. The trickle thickened and became a stream. <u>Oblivious</u>, the man continued on his way.

For a few short moments Tree-ear's thoughts wrestled with one another. *Tell him—quickly! Before he loses too much rice!*

*No! Don't say anything—you will be able to pick up the fallen rice after he rounds the bend. . . .*

Tree-ear made his decision. He waited until the man had reached the bend in the road, then ran to catch him.

"Honorable sir," Tree-ear said, panting and bowing. "As I walked behind you, I noticed that you are marking your path with rice!"

The farmer turned and saw the trail of rice. A well-built man with a broad suntanned face, he pushed his straw hat back, scratched his head, and laughed <u>ruefully</u>.

"Impatience," said the farmer. "I should have had this container woven with a double wall. But it would have taken more time. Now I pay for not waiting a bit longer." He struggled out of the *jiggeh's* straps and inspected the container. He prodded the straw to close the gap but to no avail, so he threw his arms up in <u>mock</u> despair. Tree-ear grinned. He liked the farmer's easygoing nature.

"Fetch me a few leaves, boy," said the farmer. Tree-ear complied, and the man stuffed them into the container as a temporary patch.

The farmer squatted to don the *jiggeh*. As he started walking, he called over his shoulder. "Good deserves good, <u>urchin</u>. The rice on the ground is yours if you can be troubled to gather it." ❷

> ❷ **Questioning**
> How does the farmer reward Tree-ear?

---

## Vo•cab•u•lary

**oblivious** (uh BLIV ee us) unaware
**ruefully** (ROO ful ee) regretfully
**mock** (mawk) fake; pretend
**urchin** (UR chin) a street child; a poor child who may scrounge for a living outside of the house

"Many thanks, kind sir!" Tree-ear bowed, very pleased with himself. He had made a lucky guess, and his waist pouch would soon be filled with rice.

Tree-ear had learned from Crane-man's example. <u>Foraging</u> in the woods and rubbish heaps, gathering fallen grain-heads in the autumn—these were honorable ways to <u>garner</u> a meal, requiring time and work. But stealing and begging, Crane-man said, made a man no better than a dog.

"Work gives a man dignity, stealing takes it away," he often said.

Following Crane-man's advice was not always easy for Tree-ear. Today, for example. Was it stealing, to wait as Tree-ear had for more rice to fall before alerting the man that his rice bag was leaking? Did a good deed balance a bad one? Tree-ear often pondered these kinds of questions, alone or in discussion with Crane-man.

---

## Vo•cab•u•lary

**foraging** (FOR uj ing) looking for food or other needs
**garner** (GAR nur) get; obtain

"Such questions serve in two ways," Crane-man had explained. "They keep a man's mind sharp—and his thoughts off his empty stomach."

Now, as always, he seemed to know Tree-ear's thoughts without hearing them spoken. "Tell me about this farmer," he said. "What kind of man was he?"

Tree-ear considered the question for several moments, stirring his memory. At last, he answered, "One who lacks patience—he said it himself. He had not wanted to wait for a sturdier container to be built. And he could not be bothered to pick up the fallen rice." Tree-ear paused. "But he laughed easily, even at himself."

"If he were here now, and heard you tell of waiting a little longer before speaking, what do you think he would say or do?"

"He would laugh," Tree-ear said, surprising himself with the speed of his response. Then, more slowly, "I think . . . he would not have minded."

Crane-man nodded, satisfied. And Tree-ear thought of something his friend often said: *Scholars read the great words of the world. But you and I must learn to read the world itself.* ❸ ○

**❸ Reviewing**
Go back through the story and find information that supports this statement.

---

## Answering the BIG Question

As you do the following activities, consider the Big Question:
**What's worth fighting for? What's not?**

**WRITE TO LEARN** According to Crane-man "work gives a man dignity, stealing takes it away." What is your reaction to this statement? Write your thoughts in a brief entry in your Learner's Notebook.

**LITERATURE GROUPS** Get together with two or three other students who have read this selection. Talk about why Tree-ear decided he hadn't stolen the rice. What might you have done in the same situation?

# It's Just a Question

by Nikki Grimes

Sometimes you have to fight for the attention you deserve.

## It's Just a Question

Why study
imaginary numbers
if they don't exist?
I raised my hand
to ask Mr. Peters
this question in class
but he couldn't see past
his pet students
in the front row.
As always,
he pretended
their chairs
were a wall
cutting off
the rest of us.
So I stood
and called
my question out
refusing to let him
make me feel
invisible. ○

## Answering the BIG Question

As you do the following activities, consider the Big Question:
**What's worth fighting for? What's not?**

**WRITE TO LEARN** Think about a time when you felt invisible. Describe the experience in your Learner's Notebook. How did you feel? Did you try to make others notice you? If so, how?

**LITERATURE GROUPS** Join with two or three other students who have read "It's Just a Question." Discuss how the speaker feels about the teacher's behavior, and why students resent it when teachers play favorites.

Nicholas Keen *totally* wants to go *out* with you.

I've been leaving you *messages* like *crazy.*

What?

I was just *texting* you. From *study hall.*

Oh. I'm sorry, I mean, I wasn't paying attention. I guess. There's all this—

Bygones, bygones.

So. Saturday?

Saturday?

Our date with *Nicholas,* remember? The *movie?*

You *really* look like you could use a *break.*

I can't. Not Saturday.

I have all these *letters* to write on top of homework. I mean, I have to finish my report on *Ethan Frome*, and there's a *pop quiz* in Algebra I have to study for because he *always* has pop quizzes on Monday, and—

*Letters?* What, you're writing *letters* to Mrs. Kim now?

No, it's for these reporters in *Kasnia*. They've been thrown in jail for speaking out—

They're *not* gonna get out of jail *any slower* if you go to a movie on *Saturday.*

Chandra!

At least we're almost done with that *Gilbert Swamp* thing.

So you can *stop* worrying about *the waterfowl* on top of *every* thing else.

Oops.

What? *What* oops? Keiko?

I *know* I promised I'd have the rest of the photos I took for you today.

I *forgot.* I could e-mail them to you, except they're really big files, which you need for the resolution.

It's *okay,* Keiko.

It's not *the end of the world.*

I *could* set up an FTP account on my server and—

I don't even know what that *means.*

Well, if you've got Internet access –

Keiko, it's *okay.* I'll just use the photos you took for the presentation.

Hey, Mrs. Kim.

My favorite visitor seems awfully *sad* today.

Oh. I'm sorry.

Tell me what's *wrong*.

No, I'm supposed to be here for *you*. This is *your* time, you know?

And what *I* want to do with my time—

— is hear what's *troubling* you.

*sigh* My best friend's *mad* at me because I'm so *busy* these days. She wants to go see a movie, only I *can't*, not this weekend.

And she wouldn't *listen* when I tried to explain.

A *true* friend should always listen.

It's not like that.

I guess I *did* blow her off. I said I would go before, but—there's *so much* to do!

What happened?

To *Sandy?* I don't know. I think I saw her *twice,* after graduation.

I guess we were so *busy,* we never even had time for *photographs.*

*This* is the stupidest book *ever.*

The snow's a metaphor for pointlessness.

What?

I was wondering if you could help me out with something.

And what would *that* be?

**WRITE TO LEARN**
Friends are worth fighting for. How do you manage demands on your time with your friendships? Write an entry in your Learner's Notebook about what you do to keep up with friendships that are worth fighting for.

The End

from

# I Have a Dream:

## The Life and Words of Martin Luther King, Jr.

### by Jim Haskins

---

**Martin Luther King, Jr., recalls the courage of his father.**

---

**M**artin Luther King, Sr., was a proud man who had worked hard for his education and his position. He knew he had worked harder and knew more than many whites who thought themselves better than he. He often stood up to racist whites, making his wife fearful that he would one day get himself into trouble. In the South in those days a black man who stood up to whites could be in serious danger, as the frequent <u>lynchings</u> proved. But the Reverend King didn't do anything foolish; he simply refused to bow his head and suffer ill-treatment. His behavior had a lasting effect on his children.

Martin later described two such incidents with his father.

I remembered a trip to a downtown shoestore with Father when I was still small. We had sat down in the first empty seats at the front of the store. A young white clerk came up and murmured politely:

"I'll be happy to serve you if you'll just move to those seats in the rear."

My father answered, "There's nothing wrong with these seats. We're quite comfortable here."

"Sorry," said the clerk, "but you'll have to move."

"We'll either buy shoes sitting here," my father retorted, "or we won't buy shoes at all." <u>Whereupon</u> he took me by the hand and walked out of the store. This was the first time I had ever seen my father so angry. I still remember walking down the street beside him as he muttered, "I don't care how long I have to live with this system, I will never accept it."

And he never has. I remember riding with him another day when he accidentally drove past a stop sign. A policeman pulled up to the car and said:

"All right, boy, pull over and let me see your license."

My father replied indignantly, "I'm no boy." Then, pointing to me, "This is a boy. I'm a man, and until you call me one, I will not listen to you."

## Vo•cab•u•lary

**lynchings** (LINCH ingz) the hanging of people by a mob of people and not by the law
**whereupon** (WAIR up awn) at that same moment

The policeman was so shocked that he wrote the ticket up nervously and left the scene as quickly as possible.

From before I was born, my father had refused to ride the city buses, after witnessing a brutal attack on a load of Negro passengers. ❶ He had led the fight in Atlanta to equalize teachers' salaries, and had been <u>instrumental</u> in the elimination of <u>Jim Crow</u> elevators in the courthouse. As pastor of the Ebenezer Baptist Church, where he still presides over a congregation of four thousand, he had wielded great influence in the Negro community, and had perhaps won the grudging respect of the whites. At any rate, they had never attacked him physically, a fact that filled my brother and sister and me with wonder as we grew up in this tension-packed atmosphere. ○

❶ **Distinguishing Fact from Opinion**
Is this statement a fact or an opinion? Explain.

---

## Answering the BIG Question

As you do the following activities, consider the Big Question:
**What's worth fighting for? What's not?**

**WRITE TO LEARN** Think of a time when you were unfairly excluded from a place, an activity, or a group. Write an entry in your Learner's Notebook describing how you felt and what you did about the situation.

**PARTNER TALK** With a partner, discuss the two incidents that Martin Luther King, Jr., describes. Role-play a possible conversation between him and his father after one of the incidents. What might the elder King have told his son?

---

## Vo•cab•u•lary

**instrumental** (in struh MEN tul) responsible for
**Jim Crow** (jim croh) having to do with the Jim Crow laws, which upheld segregation of blacks and whites

# PHOENIX FARM

## by Jane Yolen

**Can a better life rise from the ashes of disaster?**

We moved into Grandma's farm right after our apartment house burned down along with most of the neighborhood. Even without the fire, it had not been a good California summer, dry as popcorn and twice as salty, what with all the sweat running down our faces.

I didn't mind so much—the fire, I mean. I had hated that apartment, with its <u>pockmarked</u> walls and the gang names scribbled on the stoop. Under my bedroom window someone had painted the words "Someday, sugar, you gonna find no one in this world gonna give you sweet." The grammar bothered me more than what it said.

Mama cried, though. About the photos, mostly. And about all her shoes having burned up. She has real tiny feet and her one vanity is shoes. She can buy the model stuff for really cheap. But it's not just the photos and the shoes. She cries about everything these days. It's been that way since Daddy died.

*Ran off.* That's what Nicky says. A week before the fire. *Couldn't take it. The recession and all. No job. No hope.*

Mama says it won't be forever, but I say he died. I can deal with it that way.

And besides, we don't want him back.

So we got ready to head for Grandma's farm up in the valley, with only the clothes we'd been wearing; our cat, Tambourine; and Mama's track medals, all <u>fused</u> together. She found them when the firefighters let us go back upstairs to sort things out. Nicky grabbed a souvenir, too. His old basketball. It was flat and blackened, like a pancake someone left on the stove too long.

I looked around and there was nothing I wanted to take. Nothing. All that I cared about had made it through the fire: Mama, Nicky, and Tam. It was as if we could start afresh and all the rest of it had been burned away. ❶ But as we were going down the stairs—the iron stairs, not the wooden ones inside, which were all gone—I saw the most surprising thing. On the thirteenth step up from the bottom, tucked against the riser, was a nest. It was unburnt, unmarked, the straw that held it the

❶ **Reviewing**
How does the narrator feel about the fire and about moving away?

---

## Vo•cab•u•lary

**pockmarked** (PAWK markt ) covered with pits or depressions
**fused** (fyoozd) become united by melting

rubbed-off gold of a wheat field. A piece of red string ran through it, almost as if it had been woven on a loom. In the nest was a single egg.

It didn't look like any egg I'd ever seen before, not dull white or tan like the eggs from the store. Not even a light blue like the robin's egg I'd found the one summer we'd spent with Grandma at the farm. This was a shiny, shimmery gray-green egg with a red vein—the red thread—butting it in half.

"Look!" I called out. But Mama and Nicky were already in the car, waiting. So without thinking it all the way through—like what I was going to do with an egg, and what about the egg's mother, and what if it broke in the car or, worse, hatched— I picked it up and stuck it in the pocket of my jacket. Then, on second thought, I took off the jacket and made a kind of nest on it, and carefully carried the egg and my jacket down the rest of the stairs.

When I got into the car, it was the very first time I had ever ridden in the back all alone without complaining. And all the way to the farm, I kept the jacket-nest and its egg in my lap. All the way.

Grandma welcomed us, saying, "I'm not surprised. Didn't I tell you?" Meaning that Daddy wasn't with us. She and Mama didn't fight over it, which was a surprise on its own. Neighbors of Grandma's had collected clothes for us. It made us feel like refugees, which is an awkward feeling that makes you prickly and cranky most of the time. At least that's how I felt until I found a green sweater that exactly matches my eyes and Nicky found a Grateful Dead T-shirt. ❷ There were no shoes Mama's size. And no jobs nearby, either.

❷ **Questioning**
Why does the narrator feel cranky at first?

I stashed the egg in its jacket-nest on the dresser Mama and I shared. Nicky, being the only boy, got his own room. Mama never said a word about the egg. It was like she didn't even see it. I worried what she'd say if it began to smell.

But the days went by and the egg never did begin to stink. We got settled into our new school. I only thought about Daddy every other day. And I found a best friend right away. Nicky had girls calling him after dinner for the first time. So we were OK.

Mama wasn't happy, though. She and Grandma didn't exactly quarrel, but they didn't exactly get along, either. Being thankful to someone doesn't make you like them. And since Mama couldn't find a job, they were together all day long.

Then one evening my new best friend, Ann Marie, was over. We were doing homework together up in my room. It was one of those coolish evenings and the windows were closed, but it was still pretty bright outside, considering.

Ann Marie suddenly said, "Look! Your egg is cracking open."

I looked up and she was right. We hadn't noticed anything before, because the crack had run along the red line. When I put my finger on the rack, it seemed to <u>pulse</u>.

"Feel that!" I said.

Ann Marie touched it, then jerked back as if she had been burned. "I'm going home now," she said.

"But, Ann Marie, aren't you the one who dragged me to see all those horror movies and—"

"Movies aren't real," she said. She grabbed up her books and ran from the room.

I didn't even say good-bye. The egg had all my attention, for the gray-green shell seemed to be taking little breaths, pulsing

---

### Vo•cab•u•lary

**pulse** (puls) to expand and contract or move rhythmically, like a heartbeat

in and out, in and out, like a tiny brittle ocean. Then the crack widened, and as if there were a lamp inside, light poured out.

Nicky came in then, looking for some change on the dresser.

"Neat!" he said when he saw the light. "Do you know what kind of bird it's going to be? Did you look it up in Dad—" And then he stopped, because all of Daddy's books had been burned up. Besides, we didn't mention him anymore. And since we hadn't heard from him at all, it was like he really was dead.

"No," I said. "And I don't think it's any ordinary bird that you would find in an ordinary book."

"A lizard, you think?"

Never taking my eyes off the egg, I shook my head. How stupid could he be? With that light coming out? A dragon, maybe. Then the phone rang downstairs and he ran out of the room, expecting, I guess, that it would be Courtney or Brittany or any other of his girlfriends named after spaniels. Talking to them was more important to him than my egg.

But I continued to watch. I was the only one watching when it hatched. How such a large bird got into such a small egg, I'll never know. But that's magic for you. It rose slowly out of the egg, pushing the top part of the shell with its golden head. Its beak was golden, too, and curved like one of those Arabian swords. Its eyes were hooded and dark, without a center. When it stared at me, I felt drawn in.

The bird gave a sudden kind of shudder and humped itself farther out of the egg, and its wings were blue and scarlet and gold, all shimmery, like some seashells when they're wet. It shook out its wings, and they were wide enough to touch from one side of the dresser to the other, the individual feathers throwing off sparkles of light.

Another shudder, and the bird stood free of the egg entirely, though a piece of shell still clung to the top of one wing. I reached over and freed it, and it <u>seared</u> my fingers—the touch of the feather, not the shell. The bird's scarlet body and scaly golden feet pulsed with some kind of heat.

"What are you?" I whispered, then stuck my burnt fingers in my mouth to soothe them.

If the bird could answer me, it didn't; it just pumped its wing, which seemed to grow wider with each beat. The wind from them was a <u>Santa Ana</u>, hot and heavy and thick.

I ran to the window and flung it wide, holding the curtain aside.

The bird didn't seem to notice my efforts, but still it flew unerringly outside. I saw it land once on a fencepost; a second time, on the roof of Grandma's barn. Then it headed straight toward the city, the setting sun making a fire in its feathers.

When I couldn't see it anymore, I turned around. The room smelled odd—like the ashes of a fire, but like something else, too. Cinnamon, maybe. Or cloves.

I heard the doorbell. It rang once, then a second time. Grandma and Mama were off visiting a neighbor. Nicky was still on the phone. I ran down the stairs and flung the door wide open.

## Vo•cab•u•lary

**seared** (seerd) burned
**Santa Ana** (SAN tuh  A nuh) a strong, hot, dry wind that occurs in southern California

Daddy was standing there, a new beard on his face and a great big Madame Alexander doll in his arms.

"I got a job, baby. In Phoenix. And a house rented. With a real backyard. I didn't know about the fire, I didn't know where you all had gone. My letters came back and the phone didn't connect and . . ."

"Daddy!" I shouted, and he dropped the box to scoop me up against his chest. As I snuggled my face against his neck, I smelled the same smell: ashes and cinnamon, maybe cloves. ❸ Where my burnt fingers tangled in his hair they hurt horribly.

Grandma would be furious. Nicky and Mama might be, too. But I didn't care. There's dead. And there's not.

Sometimes it's better to rise up out of the ashes, singing. ○

❸ **Questioning**
What happens after the bird flies away?

---

## Answering the BIG Question

As you do the following activities, consider the Big Question:
**What's worth fighting for? What's not?**

**WRITE TO LEARN** Think about the way the narrator reacts to Daddy's return. How do you think Mama and Nicky will react? What do you think will happen next? Write your response to these questions in your Learner's Notebook.

**PARTNER TALK** In Greek mythology, the phoenix is a bird that is reborn by rising from the ashes of a fire. With a partner, discuss what you think the phoenix in the story stands for. What does this story have in common with the Greek myth?

# IDA BATTLES BIG OIL

by Ruth Spencer Johnson

**Find out how one woman helped to bring down the largest oil company in the United States.**

When Ida Tarbell's mother warned her not to play in the puddles that dotted their yard, she was not talking about mud puddles. She meant the pools of black oil gushing from the oil well by their front door. In 1860, three-year-old Ida lived near Oil Creek in northwestern Pennsylvania, where oil had been recently discovered.

Like many others hoping to profit from this, Ida's father started a small oil company. His business <u>prospered</u> for a number of years. Then John D. Rockefeller formed a group of oil producers into a <u>trust</u> and called it the Standard Oil Company. The railroads that shipped

## Vo•cab•u•lary

**prospered** (PRAW spurd) was financially successful
**trust** (trust) a group of legally linked companies

the oil from Tarbell's company secretly gave lower delivery rates to Standard Oil. Because of this, the trust was able to sell its oil for less, forcing smaller companies like Tarbell's out of business.

When Ida grew up, she became a famous writer for *McClure's Magazine*. Remembering how Standard Oil had crushed her father's business, Tarbell decided to uncover the story behind the giant company's success. By 1900, it was the largest trust in the country. Many people discouraged Tarbell from exposing the secrets of the powerful <u>monopoly</u>. Even her father cautioned, "Don't do it, Ida— they will ruin the magazine." ❶

**❶ Distinguishing Fact from Opinion**
Is Ida's father stating a fact or an opinion? Explain.

In spite of the warnings, Tarbell was not afraid. She planned to present a fair and accurate picture of the company. How could Standard Oil object to that? Tarbell interviewed people and searched through piles of documents and testimony to discover the truth. Some important papers had been destroyed or hidden, but Tarbell did not give up until she got all the facts.

Tarbell learned that Standard Oil had become so strong because it used unfair and dishonest business practices. For example, Standard Oil <u>conspired</u> illegally with the railroads to get cheaper delivery rates. Also, when other companies shipped oil, the railroads passed on part of the payment, called a refund, to Standard Oil. Because of these advantages, the trust could set its prices so low that smaller companies could not compete. Standard Oil even resorted to spying: It paid the railroad employees to report the scheduled shipping dates of other oil producers. Standard Oil then forced the railroads to stop those shipments.

After two years of research, Tarbell's first article about Standard Oil appeared in *McClure's*. Starting in November 1902,

---

### Vo•cab•u•lary

**monopoly** (muh NAH pul ee) a company that completely controls an industry
**conspired** (kun SPYRD) worked together with others toward a hurtful or illegal goal

19 <u>installments</u> of "The History of the Standard Oil Company" ran in the magazine. In 1904, the articles were published as a two-volume book.

In her series, Tarbell called for the American people to take a stand against greed and dishonesty. She saw a need for "an increasing scorn of unfair play—an increasing sense that a thing won by breaking the rules of the game is not worth the winning."

Thanks to Tarbell's research, Standard Oil became the focus of many investigations at both the state and federal government levels. In 1911, the U.S. Supreme Court ordered Standard Oil to break up into 38 smaller companies. Independent oil businesses would no longer have to struggle against powerful oil trusts.

Tarbell disliked the title "<u>muckraker</u>." She considered herself a historian who carefully uncovered the facts and honestly told a story. Years later, Tarbell declared that if she had the chance to rewrite the Standard Oil story, she would not change a single word. ○

## Answering the BIG Question

As you do the following activities, consider the big question:
**What's worth fighting for? What's not?**

**WRITE TO LEARN** Why do you think Ida Tarbel thought of herself as a historian rather than a muckraker? Write your response in your Learner's Notebook.

**LITERATURE GROUPS** Meet with two or three other students who have read "Ida Battles Big Oil." Talk about current events that Tarbell might tackle if she were alive today.

## Vo•cab•u•lary

**installments** (in STAWL mintz) parts in a series that takes place over time
**muckraker** (MUK rayk ur) a journalist who specializes in uncovering illegal or unfair activities

**BIG** Question

# What is the American Dream?

As you read the following selections, you will begin to think about the many possible answers to the question: **What is the American Dream?** The selections will help you understand what the American Dream means to a variety of people.

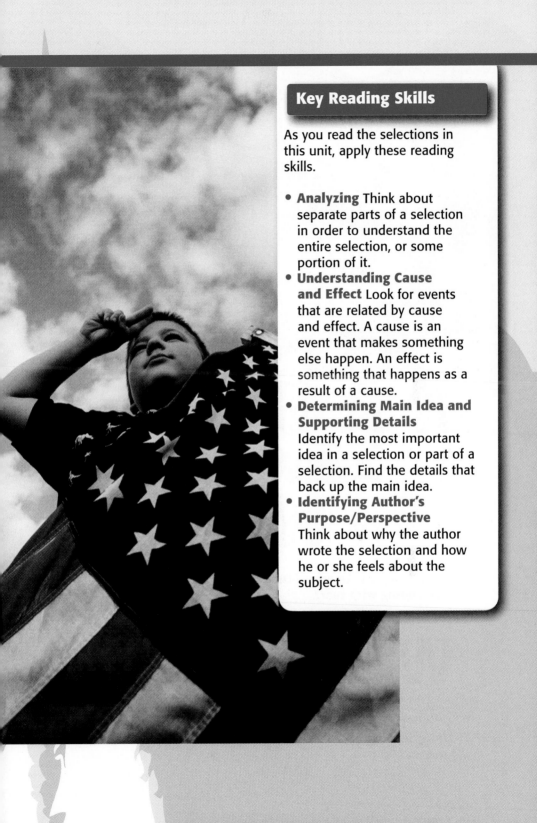

As you read the selections in this unit, apply these reading skills.

- **Analyzing** Think about separate parts of a selection in order to understand the entire selection, or some portion of it.
- **Understanding Cause and Effect** Look for events that are related by cause and effect. A cause is an event that makes something else happen. An effect is something that happens as a result of a cause.
- **Determining Main Idea and Supporting Details** Identify the most important idea in a selection or part of a selection. Find the details that back up the main idea.
- **Identifying Author's Purpose/Perspective** Think about why the author wrote the selection and how he or she feels about the subject.

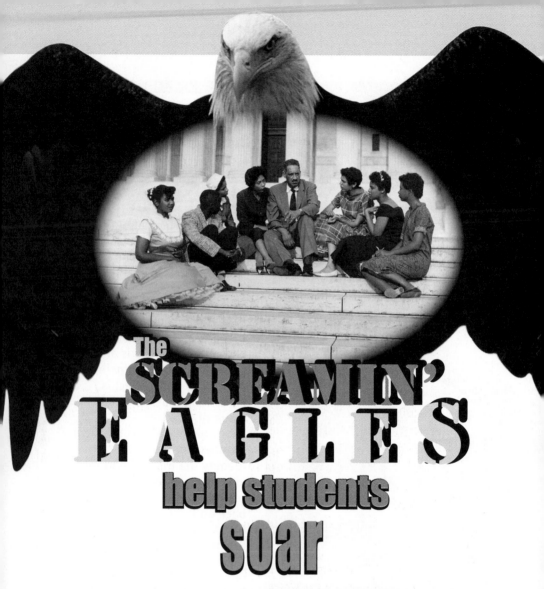

# The SCREAMIN' EAGLES help students soar

**Does reaching the American Dream of equality sometimes include coping with fear?**

**W**hat if you needed the power of the U.S. Army to protect you when you walked to school? About 50 years ago, some students actually did. But the soldiers were not the only heroes in the story. Here is a soldier's log about this most unusual assignment.

## September 24, 1957

The rumors are true. I'm going to Arkansas. On September 5, nine black students tried to start classes at Little Rock's Central High School. No blacks have ever gone there. No one would let them. The governor even sent troops from the Arkansas National Guard to stop the "Little Rock Nine" from going to Central.

Now President Eisenhower is sending 1,200 of us to make sure those kids are safe. We will arrive at the Little Rock Air Force Base today in 52 planes. We will form a <u>convoy</u> of jeeps into the city of Little Rock. Tomorrow morning, we are going to school!

## September 25, 1957, Little Rock, Arkansas ❶

**8 A.M.**

> ❶ **Determining Main Idea**
> What is the main idea of this day's entry?

Fifty of us have been stationed since dawn at the home of Mrs. Bates, head of the local NAACP (a group that works to end <u>discrimination</u>). The students are arriving: Minnijean Brown, Elizabeth Eckford, Ernest Green, Thelma Mothershed, Melba Patillo, Gloria Ray, Terrence Roberts, Jefferson Thomas, and Carlotta Walls. We all will drive to Central High. Nine of us will work as their personal bodyguards. The rest of us will patrol the halls, the entrances, and the streets.

**9 A.M.**

I thought this would be easy. Boy, was I wrong! The streets around the school were packed with people screaming, spitting, throwing rocks, and waving weapons. Some were shouting, "Two, four, six, eight, we ain't gonna <u>integrate</u>." Reporters were running, standing on cars and fences, even hanging from trees. Some of

---

### Vo•cab•u•lary

**convoy** (KAHN voy) a group of vehicles that surrounds and protects something

**discrimination** (dus krim uh NAY shun) poor treatment of people based on class or race rather than merit; prejudice

**integrate** (IN tuh grayt) to admit a racial group that was excluded before

the black reporters had been beaten badly. Until now, I did not understand the risk they took for their story.

Backs straight, <u>bayonets</u> straight, we formed a protective aisle through the crowd for the new students. Then we all walked into the building. It was their first day of school. What a first day of school.

**10 A.M.**

I took my position by the first stairway and watched the white students point, whisper, and mutter insults. Some hit and jab, too.

I am bigger and older than they are. I am armed. And I am trained not to let things bother me. I will be just fine. But I wondered—how will the new students manage?

**1 P.M.**

The lunch hour was awful. <u>Jeers</u> and insults rang out from every corner. Three white girls approached Melba, Minnijean, and Thelma. I went on alert. The white girls made a comment about the weather! They were trying to be nice! Perhaps there is hope after all. After lunch, six of us closed ranks around a group that threatened to push Melba down the stairs. They looked at our weapons and backed down.

**3 P.M.**

We headed out to a waiting car and drove the children back to the home of Mrs. Bates. We were done for the day, but the Little Rock Nine still had interviews with the press, then homework and getting ready for another day. After today, I wonder who the real warriors are.

**September 26, 1957**

It's still tough. Today I saw one of the nine get kicked, another get tripped, and still a third get jabbed with a sharp pencil. For the most part, the nine students ignore the attacks. At least, they try to. ❷

> ❷ **Understanding Cause and Effect**
> Why are some white students attacking nine African-American students?

---

## Vo•cab•u•lary

**bayonets** (bay uh NETZ) blades that fit over the end of a rifle
**jeers** (jeerz) mocking shouts

## September 27, 1957

At last, today is Friday. But the pushing, kicking, name calling, and teasing continue. Our Little Rock Nine are getting tired. I wish we could give them self-defense training. But there is no time. So we lead by example—stand straight, shoulders back, faces calm. We go about our business and help them go about theirs.

## September 30, 1957

Little Rock organizations are asking the President to cut our force. But the tension inside the school is still high.

Luckily there are some rays of hope. Today I saw a young white boy give Terry directions to his next class. I saw a girl smile at Thelma.

## October 1, 1957

We have the day off today. The President wants to see how the kids do without us.

## October 2, 1957

Reports are in. <u>Thugs</u> have been attacking the children right inside school. Luckily, the Little Rock Nine are beginning to think like warriors. They went to the principal and demanded protection. More good news—the school paper came out today with a story calling for peace.

## October 3, 1957

It is a good thing we are back in school. Someone hanged a straw figure outside the school. A student threw poison on Melba's face. Thank goodness her guard rinsed her face with water. He saved her eyesight.

## October 11, 1957

Today I was assigned to guard duty. I followed Carlotta through the halls, trying to keep her out of harm's way. It was not easy. Some children tried to get between us so they could corner her, scare her, hurt her. But we made it through the day.

---

## Vo•cab•u•lary

**thugs** (thugz) violent people

# The Screamin' Eagles Help Students Soar

## October 15, 1957

There are only nine of us now—one for each student. The Little Rock Nine do not need as much protection anymore. They keep their back straight and eyes focused in front of them. They try their best not to show pain. They keep their comments to themselves until they meet up after school. Then, at least, they have each other. Some National Guardsmen will stick around to keep watch until the end of the school year.

## November 29, 1957, Fort Campbell

I am back at Fort Campbell, but in spirit, I am still with the bravest children I ever met.

You can't protect peace by keeping your mouth shut or by ignoring trouble. In fact, you may have to speak up against cruelty and injustice—without being cruel or unjust yourself. That is what the Little Rock Nine did.

I am so proud that I protected the Little Rock Nine. They did the most important work there is: they stood up for what was right—their right to go to school, to receive an education, and to be treated fairly. ○

## Answering the BIG Question

When you do the following activities, consider the Big Question:
**What is the American Dream?**

**WRITE TO LEARN** Think of a time in your life when someone protected you or you protected another person. Write a brief entry in your Learner's Notebook about the experience.

**PARTNER TALK** Meet with a partner who has read this selection. Discuss what the soldier learned about bravery from his experience guarding the Little Rock Nine.

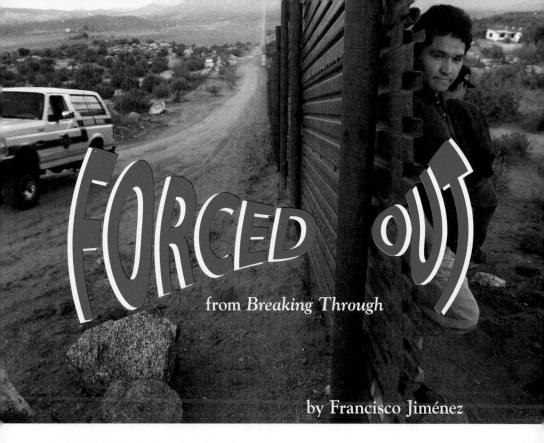

# FORCED OUT

from *Breaking Through*

by Francisco Jiménez

---

**Read about one boy's experience living as an undocumented alien in the United States.**

---

I lived in constant fear for ten long years, from the time I was four until I was fourteen years old.

It all started back in the late 1940s when Papa, Mama, my older brother, Roberto, and I left El Rancho Blanco, a small village nestled on <u>barren</u>, dry hills several miles north of Guadalajara, Jalisco, Mexico, and headed to California, hoping to leave our life of poverty behind. I remember how excited I was making the trip on a second-class train traveling north from

---

## Vo·cab·u·lary

**barren** (BAIR un) lacking vegetation

Guadalajara to Mexicali. We traveled for two days and nights. When we arrived at the United States–Mexico border, Papa told us that we had to cross the barbed-wire fence without being seen by _la migra_, the immigration officers dressed in green uniforms. During the night we dug a hole underneath the wire wall and wiggled like snakes under it to the other side. "If anyone asks you where you were born," Papa said, firmly, "tell them Colton, California. If _la migra_ catches you, they'll send you back to Mexico." We were picked up by a woman whom Papa had contacted in Mexicali. She drove us, for a fee, to a tent labor camp on the outskirts of Guadalupe, a small town on the coast. From that day on, for the next ten years, while we traveled from place to place throughout California, following the crops and living in migrant labor camps, I feared being caught by the Border Patrol.

As I got older, my fear of being deported grew. I did not want to return to Mexico because I liked going to school, even though it was difficult for me, especially English class. I enjoyed learning, and I knew that there was no school in El Rancho Blanco. Every year Roberto and I missed months of school to help Papa and Mama work in the fields. We struggled to make ends meet, especially during the winter, when work was scarce. Things got worse when Papa began to have back problems and had trouble picking crops. Luckily, in the winter of 1957, Roberto found a part-time job working year-round as a janitor at Main Street Elementary School in Santa Maria, California.

We settled in Bonetti Ranch, where we had lived in army barracks off and on for the past few years. My brother's job and

---

## Vo•cab•u•lary

**la migra** (lah MEE grah) a nickname for the U.S. Immigration and Naturalization Services, which operates the border patrols (Spanish)
**migrant** (MY grunt) traveling from one area to another in search of work
**deported** (dih PORT ud) forced to leave a country
**barracks** (BAIR iks) a building or buildings used to house soldiers

mine—thinning lettuce and picking carrots after school and on weekends—helped support our family. I was excited we had finally settled in one place. We no longer had to move to Fresno at the end of every summer and miss school for two and a half months to pick grapes and cotton and live in army tents or old garages.

But what I feared most happened that same year. I was in my eighth-grade social studies class at El Camino Junior High School in Santa Maria. I was getting ready to recite the preamble to the Declaration of Independence, which our class had to memorize. I had worked hard at memorizing it and felt confident. While I waited for class to start, I sat at my desk and recited it silently one last time:

**We hold these truths to be self-evident: that all men are created equal; that they are endowed by their creator with certain unalienable rights; that among these are life, liberty, and the pursuit of happiness . . .**

I was ready.

After the bell rang, Miss Ehlis, my English and social studies teacher, began to take roll. She was interrupted by a knock on the door. When she opened it, I saw the school principal and a man behind him. As soon as I saw the green uniform, I panicked. I felt like running, but my legs would not move. I trembled and could feel my heart pounding against my chest as though it too wanted to escape. My eyes blurred. Miss Ehlis and the officer walked up to me. "This is him," she said softly, placing her right hand on my shoulder. ❶

"Are you Francisco Jiménez?" he asked firmly. His deep voice echoed in my ears.

"Yes," I responded, wiping my tears and looking down at his large, black shiny boots. At that point I wished I were someone else, someone with a different name. My teacher had a sad and pained

❶ **Understanding Cause and Effect**
Why did Francisco panic and want to run away?

*An undocumented immigrant looks out of a police van.*

look in her eyes. I followed the <u>immigration</u> officer out of the classroom and into his car marked BORDER PATROL. I climbed in the front seat, and we drove down Broadway to Santa Maria High School to pick up Roberto, who was in his sophomore year. As cars passed by, I slid lower in the seat and kept my head down. The officer parked the car in front of the school and asked me to wait for him while he went inside the administration building.

A few minutes later, the officer returned with Roberto following him. My brother's face was as white as a sheet. The officer asked me to climb into the back seat with Robert. "*Nos agarraron, hermanito,*" Roberto said, quivering and putting his arm around my shoulder.

"Yes, they caught us," I repeated. I had never seen my brother so sad. Angry, I added in a whisper, "But it took them ten years." Roberto quickly directed my attention to the officer with a shift of his eyes and put his index finger to his lips, hushing me. The officer turned right on Main Street and headed toward Bonetti

---

### Vo•cab•u•lary

**immigration** (im uh GRAY shun)  moving to a country that is not your native country

Ranch, passing familiar sites I figured I would never see again: Main Street Elementary School; Kress, the five-and-dime store; the Texaco gas station where we got our drinking water. I wondered if my friends at El Camino Junior High would miss me as much as I would miss them.

"Do you know who turned you in?" the officer asked, interrupting my thoughts.

"No," Roberto answered.

"It was one of your people," he said, chuckling. ❷

I could not imagine whom it could have been. We never told anyone we were here illegally, not even our best friends. I looked at Roberto, hoping he knew the answer. My brother shrugged his shoulders. "Ask him who it was," I whispered.

> ❷ **Identifying Author's Purpose**
> Why do you think the author described this conversation with the officer?

"No, you ask him," he responded.

The officer, who wore large, dark green sunglasses, must have heard us, because he glanced at us through the rearview mirror and said, "Sorry, can't tell you his name."

When we arrived at Bonetti Ranch, a Border Patrol van was parked in front of our house, which was one of the many <u>dilapidated</u> army barracks that Bonetti, the owner of the ranch, bought after the Second World War and rented to farm workers. My whole family was outside, standing by the patrol car. Mama was sobbing and caressing Ruben, my youngest brother, and Rorra, my little sister. They hung on to Mama's legs like two children who had just been found after being lost. Papa stood between my two younger brothers, Trampita and Torito. Both cried silently as Papa braced himself on their shoulders, trying to ease his back pain. Roberto and I climbed out of the car and joined them. The immigration officers, who towered over

## Vo•cab•u•lary

**dilapidated** (duh LAP uh dayt ud) in a state of disrepair through neglect

everyone, searched the ranch for other undocumented residents, but found none.

We were hauled into the Border Patrol van and driven to San Luis Obispo, the immigration headquarters. There we were asked endless questions and given papers to sign. Since Papa did not know English and Mama understood only a little, Roberto translated for them. Papa showed them his green card, which Ito, the Japanese <u>sharecropper</u> for whom we picked strawberries, had helped him get years before. Mama showed birth certificates for Trampita, Torito, Rorra, and Ruben, who were born in the United States. Mama, Roberto, and I did not have documentation; we were the only ones being forced to leave. Mama and Papa did not want to separate our family. They pleaded with the immigration officer in charge to allow us to stay a few more days so that we could leave the country together. The officer finally agreed and told us we could leave on a voluntary basis. He gave us three days to report to the U.S. immigration office at the border in Nogales, Arizona.

The next morning as we were getting ready for our trip back to Mexico, I went outside and watched the school bus pick up kids from the ranch. As it drove away, I felt empty inside and had a pain in my chest. I went back inside to help pack. Papa and Mama were sitting at the kitchen table surrounded by my brothers and sister, who listened quietly as my parents discussed our trip.

## Vo•cab•u•lary

**sharecropper** (SHAIR krawp ur) a farmer who rents his or her land from the owner and pays with a part of the crop

Papa took out the metal box in which he kept our savings and counted it. "We don't have much, but we'll have to live on the other side of the border with the little we have. Maybe it'll last us until we fix our papers and come back legally," he said.

"And with God's help, we will!" Mama said. "There's no doubt."

"I am not that sure, but we'll try," Papa responded.

I was happy to hear Papa and Mama say this. I <u>relished</u> the thought of returning to Santa Maria, going back to school and not fearing *la migra* anymore. I knew Roberto felt the same. He had a sparkle in his eyes and a big smile. ❸ ○

**❸ Analyzing**
What was the American Dream for Francisco and his family?

## Answering the
## BIG Question

As you do the following activities, consider the Big Question:
**What is the American Dream?**

**WRITE TO LEARN** Francisco was forced to leave his home, his school, and his friends. How would you feel in a similar situation? Write down your ideas in a brief entry in your Learner's Notebook.

**LITERATURE GROUPS** Meet with two or three other students who have read "Forced Out." Talk about what it would be like to live in constant fear for ten years, as Francisco did.

## Vo·cab·u·lary

**relished** (REL isht) appreciated very much

# THE AMERICAN DREAM: HAPPINESS, SAY TEENS

by Miranda Hitti

---

**What do teens believe is necessary to achieve the American Dream?**

---

The American Dream is all about happiness, not careers or material goods, and it's within reach. That bright-eyed view comes from teenagers on the <u>cusp</u> of independence and their own pursuit of happiness as adults.

---

## Vo·cab·u·lary

**cusp** (kusp) edge

Nearly 640 teens aged 13-18 discussed the American Dream with Harris Interactive pollsters. The survey was conducted for the Job Shadow Coalition, which encourages young people to "shadow" workplace <u>mentors</u> to explore career possibilities.

The poll presented seven definitions of the American Dream. Participants picked the one that sounded right to them. Here are the results:

- "Simply being happy, no matter what I do" (47%)
- "Having a house, cars, and a good job" (38%)
- "Being able to provide for my family" (30%)
- "Having the career of my dreams" (27%)
- "Being rich and/or famous" (20%)
- "Owning my own business" (7%)
- "Being 'the Boss'" (5%)

Six percent chose "other" and 5% said they weren't sure. **1**

Most participants (71%) said they believe the American Dream is achievable today. More boys than girls were sure of that (75% vs. 68%).

What does it take to turn the American Dream into reality? The teens had opinions on that, too.

**1 Determining Main Idea**
Which definition of the American Dream got the most votes in the poll?

Education topped their list. A four-year or bachelor's degree is a must, said 31%. Twenty percent said a graduate degree, such as an MBA or master's degree, was needed, while 7% said a Ph.D. was required.

Twelve percent thought some college or trade school was fine, while 4% thought a high school diploma or GED would do.

## Vo·cab·u·lary

**mentors** (MEN terz) role models or guides

Education level didn't matter to 16%, and 11% weren't sure how much schooling was required.

When it came to money, the teens were split.

Many said income made no difference (28%). But 24% said it takes an income of at least $100,000 to fund the American Dream. Eighteen percent said the dream required earning at least $50,000 per year. Eleven percent weren't sure. **2**

> **2 Identifying Author's Purpose**
> Why do you think the author wrote this article?

Fewer teens thought the dream needed a salary of more than $250,000 or a million dollars a year (8% and 9%, respectively). Hardly anyone (3%) said the American Dream was doable at the lowest income level (at least $25,000 per year). ○

## Answering the BIG Question

As you do the following activities, consider the Big Question:
**What is the American Dream?**

**WRITE TO LEARN** What is your idea of the American Dream? What can you do in order to achieve it? Jot down your ideas in your Learner's Notebook.

**LITERATURE GROUPS** In a small group, discuss the definitions of the American Dream listed in the article. Poll your group to see which definition each member would choose.

**BARACK OBAMA'S**
**KEYNOTE SPEECH**

At the 2004 Democratic convention U.S. Senator Obama talks about keeping the American Dream alive.

Tonight is a particular honor for me because—let's face it—my presence on this stage is pretty unlikely. My father was a foreign student, born and raised in a small village in Kenya. He grew up herding goats, went to school in a tin-roof shack. His father—my grandfather was a cook—a <u>domestic</u> servant to the British.

## Vo·cab·u·lary

**domestic** (duh MES tik) having to do with home and family

But my grandfather had larger dreams for his son. Through hard work and <u>perseverance</u> my father got a scholarship to study in a magical place, America, that shone as a beacon of freedom and opportunity to so many who had come before.

While studying here, my father met my mother. She was born in a town on the other side of the world, in Kansas. Her father worked on oil rigs and farms through most of the Depression. The day after Pearl Harbor my grandfather signed up for duty, joined Patton's army, marched across Europe. Back home, my grandmother raised their baby and went to work on a bomber assembly line. After the war, they studied on the G.I. Bill, bought a house through F.H.A., and later moved west all the way to Hawaii in search of opportunity.

And they, too, had big dreams for their daughter. A common dream, born of two continents.

My parents shared not only an <u>improbable</u> love, they shared an <u>abiding</u> faith in the possibilities of this nation. They would give me an African name, Barack, or "blessed," believing that in a tolerant America your name is no barrier to success. They imagined me going to the best

## Vo•cab•u•lary

**perseverance** (pur suh VIR uns) dedication; determination
**improbable** (im PRAW buh bul) unlikely
**abiding** (uh BY ding) enduring; lasting

schools in the land, even though they weren't rich, because in a generous America you don't have to be rich to achieve your potential. **1**

**1 Determining Main Idea and Supporting Details**
What dreams did Obama's parents have for their country and their son?

They are both passed away now. And yet, I know that, on this night, they look down on me with great pride.

I stand here today, grateful for the <u>diversity</u> of my heritage, aware that my parents' dreams live on in my two precious daughters. I stand here knowing that my story is part of the larger American story, that I owe a debt to all of those who came before me, and that, in no other country on earth, is my story even possible.

Tonight, we gather to <u>affirm</u> the greatness of our nation—not because of the height of our skyscrapers, or the power of our military, or the size of our economy. Our pride is based on a very simple <u>premise</u>, summed up in a declaration made over two hundred years ago: "We hold these truths to be self-evident, that all men are created equal. That they are endowed by their Creator with certain inalienable rights. That among these are life, liberty, and the pursuit of happiness."

This is the true genius of America—a faith in simple dreams, an insistence on small miracles. That we can tuck in our children at night and know that they are fed and clothed and safe from harm. That we can say what we think, write what we think, without hearing a sudden knock on the door. That we can have an idea and start our own business without paying a bribe. That we can participate in the political process without fear of <u>retribution</u>, and that our votes will be counted, at least most of the time.

This year, in this election, we are called to reaffirm our values and our commitments, to hold them against a hard reality and see

## Vo•cab•u•lary

**diversity** (dih VER sih tee) variety; range; assortment
**affirm** (uh FURM) insist; confirm
**premise** (PREH mus) basis; foundation; principle
**retribution** (reh truh BYOO shun) revenge; retaliation

how we are measuring up, to the legacy of our <u>forbearers,</u> and the promise of future generations.

And fellow Americans, Democrats, Republicans, Independents—I say to you tonight: we have more work to do. More work to do for the workers I met in Galesburg, Illinios, who are losing their union jobs at the Maytag plant that's moving to Mexico, and now are having to compete with their own children for jobs that pay seven bucks an hour. More to do for the father that I met who was losing his job and choking back the tears, wondering how he would pay $4,500 a month for the drugs his son needs without the health benefits he counted on. More to do for the young woman in East St. Louis, and thousands more like her, who has the grades, has the drive, has the will, but doesn't have the money to go to college.

Now don't get me wrong. The people I meet—in small towns and big cities, in diners and office parks—they don't expect government to solve all their problems. They know they have to work hard to get ahead— and they want to.

Go into the collar counties around Chicago, and people will tell you they don't want their tax money wasted, by a welfare agency or by the Pentagon.

Go into any inner city neighborhood, and folks will tell you that government alone can't teach our kids to learn—they know that parents have to teach, that children

## Vo•cab•u•lary

**forbearers** (FOR bair ers) ancestors

can't achieve unless we raise their expectations and turn off the television sets and <u>eradicate</u> the <u>slander</u> that says a black youth with a book is acting white. They know those things.

People don't expect government to solve all their problems. But they sense, deep in their bones, that with just a slight change in priorities, we can make sure that every child in America has a decent shot at life, and that the doors of opportunity remain open to all. ❷

They know we can do better. And they want that choice. ○

> ❷ **Identifying Author's Perspective**
> What is Barack Obama's definition of the American Dream?

---

## Answering the BIG Question

As you do the following activities, consider the Big Question:
**What is the American Dream?**

**WRITE TO LEARN** Obama is grateful to his family and his country for the life he has been able to have. What are you grateful for? What makes your life in this country full of opportunities and possibilities? Write a brief entry in your Learner's Notebook and back it up with examples from your life.

**PARTNER TALK** Obama says that "doors of opportunity" should stay open to all Americans. With a partner, discuss what you think this statement means. Do you feel that you are free to pursue your own version of the American Dream? Why or why not?

---

## Vo•cab•u•lary

**eradicate** (ih RAD ih kayt) get rid of; exterminate
**slander** (SLAN dur) a false and damaging statement

# Building

# Bridges

by Andrea Davis Pinkney

---

**When you dream big, what could ever stop you?**

---

At first, Mama Lil said it plain and simple: "No."

Then, like always, she spoke her full mind. "Bebe, get that backward idea out your head. That grit work ain't no place for you. And besides, I ain't never heard of no girls to be doing *that.* You need to be getting yourself a real summer job, something civilized."

We'd just finished Sunday breakfast. Mama Lil had fried up a batch of Dunbar's ham, the meat we ate only on Sundays, holidays, and special occasions—my all-time favorite.

Mama Lil pushed her breakfast plate aside and centered her ashtray. She took a final drag on her cigarette. Through the haze of smoke that clouded her small, tight face, she spoke slow and deliberate. "And don't ask me again about signing that permission paper," she said. "I ain't gonna be the one who allows you to take part in such foolishness."

I leaned back in my kitchen chair, my arms folded tight. The chair's vinyl stuck to the skin on my shoulders, taping itself to the place where my T-shirt scooped down at my back. It was as if, like Mama Lil, that chair wanted to hold me in its clutches.

I'd been living with Mama Lil since I was six, when my own mama and daddy were taken by the Walcott apartment building fire. Lillian Jones was my mom's mother. Everybody on our street called my grandmother Mama Lil, and that's what I called her, too. She was a mama to everybody, it seemed, always <u>scolding</u>

---

## Vo·cab·u·lary

**scolding** (SKOLD ing) talking to angrily; disciplining

the other neighborhood kids about playing their music too loudly in the street, or hanging out too long on the front stoop of our house. Mama Lil and I had been butting heads ever since I could remember. And the older I got, the more at odds we were.

Mama Lil hated the six studs I wore in my left ear; I hated the <u>tacky</u> red wig she pulled down close to her eyebrows whenever her hair wasn't done.

She thought I weighed too much and dressed badly; I thought she smoked too much and overdid it with her fake gold chains. Time after time, she'd ask me, "How you ever gonna land a decent man with them chunky arms and those T-shirts that put your navel on parade? No self-respecting seventeen-year-old should be letting it all hang out like *that*."

Whenever Mama Lil got on her "self-respecting seventeen-year-old" sermon, I came back with a warning under my breath: "When some homey *tries* to snatch all that shiny tin off your seventy-three-year-old neck, don't come crying to me."

If Mama Lil really wanted to heap it on, she'd start nagging me about my hair. "Child," she liked to say, "them natty braids you call dreadlocks look like the fright 'do of a zombie."

Yeah, over the years Mama Lil and I had thrown a lot of dissing words back and forth. But then, too, I had a sister-to-sister connection to Mama Lil that not many kids had with their grandmas. I could talk to her real direct. I could tell her the deal, straight up.

Mama Lil and I didn't beat around the bush because all we had was each other. There was no time to waste on half-spoken words. I was Mama Lil's only true family, and she was the only real parent I had. If I ever left her, she'd have nobody; and if she passed on, I'd be alone in this world. ❶

❶ **Understanding Cause and Effect** Why would Bebe be alone in the world if Mama Lil died? What happened to Bebe's parents?

## Vo•cab•u•lary

**tacky** (TAK ee) cheap and in bad taste

For weeks I'd been asking Mama Lil to let me join the youth renovation team, a group of kids that had been chosen by city officials to work with a squad of contract engineers to help repair the Brooklyn Bridge. The project would last the summer, pay good money, and help me get to college, where I wanted to study engineering. The whole thing sure beat flipping Big Macs at Mickey Dee's.

But Mama Lil wasn't having it. To her, I was "stooping to do a bunch of low-down mess-work." Truth be told, Mama Lil was scared of something she didn't know. She hardly ever left our neighborhood in Brooklyn; to her, the Brooklyn Bridge was a mystery.

And I think that deep down Mama Lil was afraid something bad would happen to me, the same way it happened to my mama and daddy. Also, Mama Lil couldn't read or write very well—I read most of her mail to her, and helped her sign her checks—and she hated to admit it. The two-page <u>consent</u> form she had to sign, giving me permission to work on the bridge project, was a challenge to her pride.

Then there was the fact that I would be the only girl working with the bridge crew. (My acceptance letter said few girls had applied; of those who did, I was the only qualified candidate, based on my grades.) Mama Lil thought it just wasn't right that I'd be working on a project staffed only with boys and men. "If God had meant you to do a man's work, he would have made you a man. It's that simple," she said.

All these strikes stood against me ever getting to work on that bridge. But the biggest obstacle of all, the thing that made Mama Lil the most stubborn, was my dream of becoming an engineer. Mama Lil didn't fully understand what an engineer was. I'd tried to explain it to her; I'd shown her my sketchbook full of drawings of city structures and machines, but Mama Lil didn't *know* any engineers. She'd never seen one at work.

---

## Vo·cab·u·lary

**renovation** (ren uh VAY shun) repair; improvement
**consent** (kun SENT) agree to

And to make matters worse, she'd taken it upon herself to ask her friends down at Rimley's Beauty Parlor about engineering. They'd convinced her that I was headed down the wrong path. "Ain't no black woman doing no engine-ing," she'd said.

"Engin*eer*ing," I'd corrected.

Mama Lil said, "Whatever you call it, it's a white man's work. You ain't got no place messing with it. We should stick with our own kind, Bebe—colored women trying to cross the white man's line is asking for trouble." ❷

**❷ Determining Main Idea and Supporting Details** List the reasons why Mama Lil is set against Bebe working on the bridge.

In some respects, Mama Lil was right. Black folks did need to stick together, no doubt. But not in the way Mama Lil meant. And it *was* true that there weren't many black women engineers. I knew from the get-go that if I hoped to become an engineer, my road ahead would be lonely and hard. But I wanted to build bridges more than anything. And working on the bridge project was the first step—a step that I needed Mama Lil's help to make. A step that started right here in her tiny kitchen.

The last of Mama Lil's cigarette smoke lingered between us.

"I wish you'd lay off on those Carltons," I said, pushing the smoke away with a single wave of my hand.

Mama Lil rose from the table. She took her ashtray with her. "I'm trying to quit, Bebe, you know that," she said. "Carltons have less tar, less nicotine. They're better for you," she reasoned.

"And I'm Miss America," I huffed.

At the sink, Mama Lil lit another cigarette, then started washing the dishes. "Look, missy," she scolded, "don't be taking your bad mood out on me. You get cranky every time we talk about that nasty job you want to get." Mama Lil turned her back to me and began to fill the sink with soapy water.

"It's *not* nasty," I said, my voice rising. "This is good work, Mama Lil. I'd be employed by the city—by the mayor."

Mama Lil was busy lathering the greasy skillet she'd used to fry the ham. With her back to me—she had strong back muscles that showed beneath her blouse—she said, "Bebe, I don't care if you're working for the King of Siam. Hammering a bridge together is not respectable work for a young lady."

"But, Mama Lil, working on the bridge isn't just—"

"—Don't get me wrong, Bebe—" Mama Lil kept her back to me, "all those pretty pictures you draw in the tablet of yours are real nice. But, child, doing that to earn a living is a pipe dream. *White* folks can pay their bills by sitting around doodling. We just don't got it like that."

I leaned my forehead onto the heels of both my hands. The kitchen hung quiet for a moment, its only sound the scrub of Brillo scratching the ham skillet. Mama Lil cleaned in a steady, determined rhythm. With each scrub, she hunched further over the sink, giving that pan every bit of strength she had. "This damn grease is stubborn," she said, her back muscles tense with effort.

"*You're* stubborn," I spat in a low voice. But Mama Lil didn't hear me. She just kept on scrubbing.

That evening Mama Lil dozed off in front of her little black-and-white television set. The blue cast of the TV's light danced across her face, softening its tired lines. Mama Lil wheezed out small, breathy snores. She was sinking into the kind of sleep that often kept her on the couch—TV babbling on—all night.

I locked Mama Lil safe inside the house, and, with my sketchbook tucked firm under my arm, I headed for the street. As I walked our noisy avenue, I took in the lights and people who dotted the darkness. I thought hard about Mama Lil's mule-headed words: "Ain't no black woman doing no engineering . . . trying to cross the white man's line is asking for trouble."

I walked fast and furious for blocks and blocks, the warm summer air heaving in my lungs. My armpits had grown sticky with perspiration. The hair at my temples began to crimp with sweat. Finally, I stopped under a streetlight—a streetlight that was my hiding place—on a quiet corner, just off Shore Street. I leaned into the streetlight's cold aluminum pole, letting my breath slow itself down.

Ahead, in the distance, stood the Brooklyn Bridge. This was the best spot in Brooklyn's Red Hook section for seeing the bridge. I'd come to this corner and studied the bridge a million times. And on every one of those times, I was taken with what I'd come to call Brooklyn Belle.

I never got tired of looking out at its steel girders and iron cables—at its beautiful crisscross rafters that had started out in somebody's imagination, had been put to paper, formalized in an engineer's plans, then woven together, bolt by bolt. Now Belle was a powerful giant who carried all kinds of people to all kinds of places, day after day.

At night Belle was dressed in tiny lights that spanned her limbs. On a cloudless night like this one, she was a sight like no other sight in the whole city. Jeweled in light. *Beautiful.*

My fingers had tensed into fists at my sides, fists full of strength and eagerness. I uncurled my knuckles and shook them free of their strain. Then I reached into my jacket pocket—where my consent form for the bridge project had been neatly folded for days—and pulled out my pencil. Slowly, I flipped through the pages of my sketchbook. I'd drawn Belle in the high-noon light, at sunset, on snowy days, and on foggy twilight mornings.

---

### Vo•cab•u•lary

**perspiration** (per spuh RAY shun) sweat
**crimp** (krimp) curl tightly
**girders** (GUR durz) large, strong beams used for construction

My favorite sketches were those of Belle during rush hour, when cars and taxis danced like <u>trinkets</u> along her outstretched beams.

Tonight I'd draw Belle with her lighted cape. I sketched slowly at first, then faster, my pencil working with the speed of my excitement— the thrill that worked me over every time I sketched that bridge.

I was proud of my drawings (I liked to think of them as portraits), but with each page they showed a sad truth about Belle: She needed repair. She was some forty years older than Mama Lil. And as lovely as she was, she had some serious rough spots—<u>corroded</u> cables, rust, chipped paint, and plain old grit that had built up over the decades. That bridge renovation project needed me; and I needed it, in more ways than I could count. **3**

**3 Analyzing**
Why does Bebe need the bridge project? Why is it so important to her?

The air had grown sticky, moistening the pages of my sketchbook. It was getting late. The orange glow of the streetlight above my head flickered in the blue-black night. I slid my pencil back to its pocket, and headed for home.

If I'd had a bet on it, I'd have put my money down that Mama Lil hadn't missed me one bit. She was probably snoring

## Vo•cab•u•lary
**trinkets** (TRING kits) jewelry or charms
**corroded** (kuh ROHD ud) rotted; worn

up a storm by now. And her TV was most likely still blipping its <u>hues</u> onto her face, sending its random talk-show chatter around her living room.

A week passed. A week of Mama Lil and I not speaking about the bridge project, or the permission form that was due—signed by her—in four days, when the renovation was supposed to begin.

We talked about plenty of other things—the hell-hot summer heat, the tomatoes at Key food, Oprah's new look—but we sidestepped talk about the bridge altogether. And with each avoidance, with each conversation about nothing at all, the Brooklyn Bridge loomed larger. It was as if Belle were sitting smack center in Mama Lil's living room, with <u>gridlocked</u> traffic fighting for space on her pavement. ❹ If I didn't get my consent form signed, I would <u>forfeit</u> my place on the project. Every time I tried to bring it up, Mama Lil twisted her lips and raised her hand. "Don't be bringing that mess in here, Bebe. There ain't no more discussing to do."

❹ **Identifying Author's Purpose**
Why does the author make the bridge seem like a person?

As the days passed, I grew more anxious, and more angry at Mama Lil's attitude. On the Saturday night before the project was to start, Mama Lil did something that got me real mad. She brought home a summer job application from Rimley's Beauty Parlor, where she and her gossipy friends spent their days.

As Mama Lil lifted the application from her purse, she had the nerve to say, "Bebe, I went and done you a big favor." I give Mama Lil a hard sideways stare.

She kept talking. "Vernice Rimley needs someone to sweep hair and clean her sinks. She can't pay you nothing to start, but

---

**Vo•cab•u•lary**

**hues** (hyooz) shades of colors
**gridlocked** (GRID lawkt) stuck in traffic that is not moving
**forfeit** (FOR fit) give up

you'd get a heap of training. By next summer you'd be doing perms and manicures, and getting tips on top of a regular salary. And you could even bring your paper tablet, so you can draw during your breaks."

Mama Lil put the application down on the coffee table between us. As she spoke, she tapped it with her finger, emphasizing her words. "Bebe, if you put your mind to it, you could be awfully good at doing hair. Give it a chance, child," she urged.

My forehead and upper lip grew moist with the sweat that anger brings on. I wiped the back of my hand across my mouth, feeling my words jump to my throat before I spoke them.

Mama Lil lit a Carlton. She sat back on her sofa, blowing smoke straight ahead. Her eyes avoided mine. "Mama Lil," I began, "*look* at me."

But Mama Lil was sinking deeper into her stubbornness. She leaned her head back, inhaled on her cigarette, and closed her eyes to release another stream of smoke. "I'm enjoying my cig, Bebe," she said. "It tastes better with my eyes closed."

I leaned in the doorway, my anger rising. "Mama Lil, your eyes are *always* closed. *Closed* to seeing me." Mama Lil's lips curled around the tip of her Carlton, letting the cigarette dangle for a moment.

I said, "I don't want to spend my summer sweeping hair. The bridge is where my heart's at, Mama Lil."

Mama Lil shifted on her couch pillow. I could see her eyes roaming beneath their lids. She took another drag, a heavy one this time, and blew out a long, quick breath. She was doing her best to tune me out. "Yeah, that's right," I said, my voice strained with frustration, "blow me away. Try to make me and my dreams disappear, like your puffs of smoke!" I was hollering now, full out. I kicked the doorjamb with the toe of my sneaker. "Damn!"

Mama Lil opened her eyes in search of the cat-shaped ashtray she kept on her cofffee table. She tapped her ashes into the cat's

face, then <u>aligned</u> her gaze with mine. Her eyes looked weary, her expression pained. She set her Carlton along the cat's ceramic tail and let it <u>smolder</u>. She sighed. "Bebe, I'm an old woman. I ain't got much to look forward to in this life—not many of my own dreams to go after." Mama Lil's voice trailed off to silence. Then her face softened, and for the first time ever, I saw Mama Lil's eyes fill with regret. "What little bit of dreaming I got left in me," she said, "I'm putting to you."

I licked my lips and listened. Mama Lil had more to say. "But I can't dream your dreams, Bebe. Working on that old bridge so that you can study some high-tone thing like engineering is a far-off notion that don't fit in this old woman's way."

Mama Lil let out a heavy breath. Then she admitted what we'd both known all along. "Your dreams are the kind that'll take you away from here, Bebe—away from your Mama Lil. You got big hopes, child, but they gonna leave me alone, by myself." **5**

I shrugged.

Mama Lil said, "That's an upsetting truth, Bebe. It makes my heart hurt every time I think on it." The cigarette

> **5 Understanding Cause and Effect**
> What is the real reason Mama Lil doesn't want Bebe to work on her bridge project?

---

## Vo•cab•u•lary

**aligned** (uh LYND) lined up
**smolder** (SMOHL dur) burn quietly

had burned to ash. Its smoke had gone, but its heavy odor remained in the room.

Mama Lil was right. My dreams *would* take me away from her.

I wanted to comfort her, but I wasn't willing to back out on the bridge project, or give up my plans for becoming an engineer. I knelt next to the couch cushion where Mama Lil sat and took both her hands in mine.

"Mama Lil, I got to find *my* way," I said slowly. "If that bridge renovation wasn't tapping on my soul, I'd go ahead and sweep hair down at Rimley's."

For once, Mama Lil was looking into my face, hearing my words. Her eyes were filled with sad <u>acknowledgment</u>.

"Let me go, Mama Lil. Let me dream," I pleaded softly.

Mama Lil sat as still as a statue. I gently pulled my hands away from hers and reached into my pocket to find the bridge project consent form. I unfolded the thick carboned papers and set them on the coffee table, next to the application from Rimley's. "Mama Lil," I said carefully, "if you don't sign this—if you *won't* sign it—I'll sign it myself. I been helping you sign checks and letters for years now. I can sign your name on this consent form, and nobody'll know the difference."

Mama Lil's eyes began to dart. She looked from me to the consent form to the Rimley's application, and back to me again.

"I don't want to cross you, Mama Lil," I said, "but I will if I have to—to do what makes my soul feel right. To dream my dreams."

Mama Lil reached for her pack of Carltons, which were resting on the arm of her sofa. She felt for a cigarette, but the package was empty. I smoothed the consent form with my palm. "You want me to read you what it says?" I asked.

Mama Lil shook her head. "Leave it be," she insisted. "Let me sit with it awhile."

---

## Vo•cab•u•lary

**acknowledgment** (ik NAW lij mint) agreement or acceptance

I could feel my face growing warm again with perspiration. Night had fallen fully now, but Mama Lil's cramped living room still <u>sweltered</u> from the daytime heat. I could hear the boys on our block gathering to play their music on the corner. Usually Mama Lil would call from the window, hassling them to "turn that blasted noise down." But all she said was, "Bebe, get on to bed. It's getting late." I rose to my feet, hovering over Mama Lil, who, for the first time ever, looked small and sunken in her seat. "The bridge project starts tomorrow morning," I reminded her.

Mama Lil shrugged. "I know good and well when it starts, Bebe. You've told me twenty times over."

That night, the night before I was to report to the bridge project, I lay awake. I was afraid Mama Lil would doze off in front of her TV and forget about the consent form. Or that the detailed instructions on the two-page sheet would frustrate her, and she wouldn't make the effort to read it through. And worse than that, I feared Mama Lil would set fire to the form with her cigarette lighter.

When I finally fell asleep, all kinds of strange dreams danced in my head: Mama Lil crossing a bridge made of Carlton cigarettes; my sketchbook filling itself with senseless scribbles; the hair from the floor of Rimley's Beauty Parlor floating up and clinging to my face, making it hard for me to breathe. **6**

> **6 Analyzing**
> How would you interpret Bebe's dream?

I awoke to the smell of Dunbar's ham coming from the kitchen. The sun hadn't risen; twilight slowly approached. I listened for Mama Lil's TV, but all I heard was crackling grease and the shuffle of Mama Lil's feet against the kitchen tile.

My clock said 5:36. The bridge renovation crew was scheduled to meet at 7:00 at the Tillary Street entrance to the bridge. I threw on my muscle T-shirt and jeans and grabbed my sketchbook.

---

## Vo•cab•u•lary

**sweltered** (SWEL turd) very hot

When I got to the kitchen, my place was set. Mama Lil scurried betweeen the stove and the table, setting down napkins, pouring orange juice, flipping the ham as it rustled in the skillet. She didn't even see me come into the kitchen. "Hey, Mama Lil," I said.

Mama Lil peered at me over the top of her narrow glasses, glasses she wore only for reading. Glasses that hung from the chain of one of her junk jewelry necklaces. "Sit, Bebe, your ham's ready," she said. I shrugged and slid into my chair. The sun was full in the sky, zigzagging its light across the kitchen table. The hands on the kitchen clock were settling on 6:00.

Mama Lil served both our plates. She sat down across from me and started eating. She was acting like it was any other morning, chatting on about her late-night comedy show and the pigeons that nested on the ledge of her bedroom window. I was certain she'd done away with the consent form for the bridge project, and was doing her best to ignore the whole thing.

I ate in silence, wondering if the bridge crew leader would let me on the project without signed permission. I'd have to leave for the site soon, if I wanted to get there on time.

Mama Lil hadn't stopped talking. Now she was on to something about the high price of cornmeal.

I finished my last bit of ham, and interrupted. "Mama Lil," I said firmly, "I'm going to the bridge."

Mama Lil steadied her glasses. She took a heavy breath. "I know, Bebe," she said, nodding, "I know."

That's when Mama Lil reached into the pocket of her

housedress and pulled out the consent form. "You gonna need this," she said, sliding the papers across the table.

I unfolded the form, which had become worn and crumpled. But Mama Lil hadn't signed it. It was the same as it had always been. Mama Lil could see the upset pinching at my face. "Now hold it, Bebe," she said, "don't be so quick to put on that down-in-the-mouth expression."

"But you didn't sign the form, Mama Lil, and you know I can't—"

"Calm down, child." Mama Lil's tone was solid. She said, "You're jumping out the gate too fast."

"The project's gonna start without me!" I snapped.

Mama Lil leaned into the table toward me. Her eyes looked red-tired. Before I could speak another heated word, Mama Lil said, "I been up most the night, Bebe—thinking, praying, and trying my best to read that <u>confounded</u> permission paper. They sure got a whole bunch of words typed on that thing, just to say I'm gonna let you help fix a bridge."

I could feel my whole body fill with relief. Mama Lil said,

## Vo•cab•u•lary

**confounded** (kun FOWND ud) darned

"I may not know how to read that good, but I *do* know that I ain't supposed to sign something I ain't fully read."

Mama Lil pushed her glasses up further on her nose. They were speckled with dots of grease that had sprung from the hot ham skillet. "Will you help me read the permission paper, Bebe?" she asked. "Will you help me understand what it's saying to me?"

I slid my chair to Mama Lil's side of the table. Together, we read the consent form, line by line. When we were done, Mama Lil took a pen from her housedress pocket. She held it awkwardly and signed the form with her crooked handwriting.

She gave her signature a good looking-over. Her face filled with satisfaction. Then she folded the form and pressed it into my hand. "Bebe, that bridge is lucky to have you," she said.

I hugged Mama Lil good and hard, then I got up to go. Just before I left the kitchen, I turned and smiled big, right at her. "Yeah, it is," I said. **7** ○

**7 Identifying Author's Purpose**
Why does the author tell the story from Bebe's point of view?

---

## Answering the BIG Question

As you do the following activities, consider the Big Question:
**What is the American Dream?**

**WRITE TO LEARN** What kind of work would "make your soul feel right"? Write an entry in your Learner's Notebook about the job of your dreams. Why would it make you feel the way Bebe feels about the Brooklyn Bridge?

**LITERATURE GROUPS** Meet with two or three other students who have read "Building Bridges." Talk about what might happen after the end of the story. If you were to write the next chapter in the lives of Bebe and Mama Lil, what events would it include?

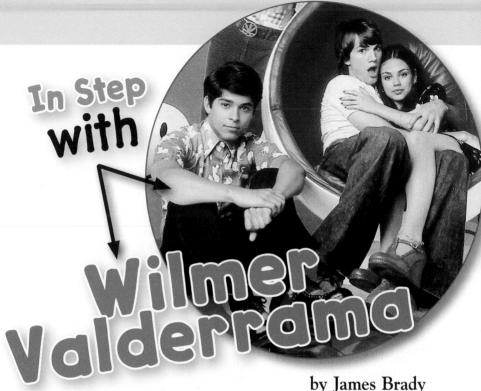

# In Step with Wilmer Valderrama

### by James Brady

**What's it like to come here from another country—and hit it big?**

This was a Friday morning in L.A., and Wilmer Valderrama was calling me from his bachelor pad in the Valley. He was getting ready to take off for work to shoot another episode playing the character Fez on *That '70s Show*, now in its eighth and maybe last season.

"It's still going great, still winning its time slot," says Wilmer, whose contract with the Fox series is now up. "I don't know if I'm going to renew it," he told me. "I'm so busy, it's crazy—all the work I've got." So he's making plenty of money?

"Oh man!" he said.

Wilmer's Spanish accent is still <u>discernible</u>, but his English is fluent and <u>colloquial</u>. He came to L.A. when he was 14, speaking

## Vo·cab·u·lary

**discernible** (dih SUR nuh bul) apparent; noticeable
**colloquial** (kuh LOH kwee ul) informal; conversational

virtually no English. He was born in Miami but was brought up in Venezuela from age 3 to 14. Now he's 25 and a one-man showbiz cottage industry still marveling at having achieved his own personal version of "the American dream."

The busy young actor—whose pals call him "Big Wil" even though he's only 5 feet 8—has his own production company, named WV Productions. "I have a great creative platform now," he told me. "And I'm going to use it."

When I asked what his next big thing was, Wilmer became very enthused. "I created a new reality show for MTV," he said. "You ever see the movie *8 Mile*? I created an *8 Mile* with laughs! It's a competition called *Yo Mama*. We go to cities around L.A. and get a bunch of kids at random and let them talk smack—you know: 'Yo mama's this, yo mama's that . . .' The funniest, the most creative of them will battle it out before a live audience. We need a new generation of reality shows. That's the idea here."

But even for MTV, won't the language be pretty rough? "The more <u>profanity</u> you use," Wilmer said, "the less creative you look. They discipline themselves. MTV guaranteed us 20 episodes. I'm the host and executive producer." So he has money in this thing? "Sure," Wilmer answered. "In Hollywood, to make real money, you have to own a piece of it."

Today Wilmer is <u>savoring</u> a life that a few years back seemed impossibly distant. He recently was cast in the new film version of the '70s TV series *CHiPs*. On top of performing and producing, he even has a clothing line, Calavena, due out soon, and he co-owns three restaurants. As Wilmer said happily, "It's crazy, man." ❶

> **❶ Determining Main Idea**
> What version of the American dream has Valderrama achieved?

---

## Vo•cab•u•lary

**profanity** (proh FAN uh tee) curse or swear words
**savoring** (SAY vur ing) enjoying something slowly; relishing

### Brady's Bits

Wilmer Valderrama's parents live five minutes away, and he has two sisters ages 24 and 17 and a 5-year-old brother. Wilmer has been linked in the gossip columns with such beauties as Mandy Moore and Lindsay Lohan. When I asked if he fell in and out of love every week or just occasionally, I got a big laugh. As a youngster in high school, struggling to learn English, Wilmer went out for school plays, hoping it would help him with the language. It did. Antonio Banderas's film *Desperado* was released around that time and, Wilmer told me, "it became cool to have an accent." He's since gotten to know Banderas. Wilmer had been in Mexico before we talked, shooting a picture that's still, he said, "top secret." He's also doing a voice for a new Disney animated TV series, *Handy Manny*, airing this month, and he has two new films in the can: *The Darwin Awards*, a comedy/adventure with Winona Ryder and Joseph Fiennes, and a fantasy, *El Muerto*. "*El Muerto* is based on the most dramatic comic book ever," he said. "It's about the pain of losing, of dying, but I throw in a few little funny things." Then he added: "I can't do a hero with a straight face." ○

## Answering the BIG Question

As you do the following activities, consider the Big Question:
**What is the American Dream?**

**WRITE TO LEARN** What do you think it would be like to go from being unknown to being a celebrity? What do you think you would enjoy most about being famous? What would you enjoy the least? Write your responses in a brief entry in your Learner's Notebook.

**PARTNER TALK** Get together with another student who has read the same selection and discuss your reactions with each other. How are your reactions the same and how are they different? What can you learn from each other?

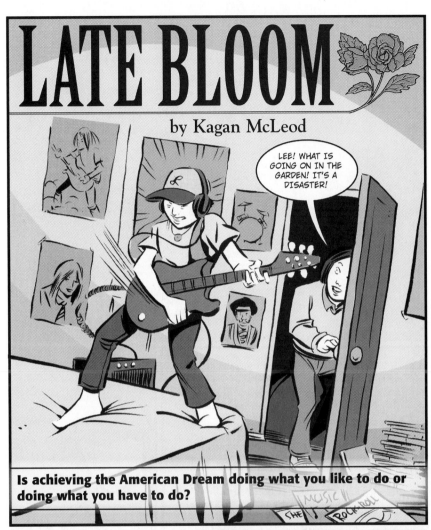

Is achieving the American Dream doing what you like to do or doing what you have to do?

NOW FOR THE CLEANUP!

WHAT THE --?

DAD?

OWW!

259

**WRITE TO LEARN**
Think about the sacrifices Lee's father made for his family. How did he help his children achieve the American Dream? Write your thoughts in your Learner's Notebook.

# 5Ways

## TEENS CAN
### spend smarter for a cleaner, greener earth

**How can you help the environment by changing your spending habits?**

Washington, DC—Earth Day 2004, April 22 was celebrated in large and small ways by millions of people around the world, including many teens. Although many people think it requires a lot of time and money to help keep the Earth protected, small changes can make a big difference.

# Top Actions Youth Can Take for a Better Planet

- Need a lot of notebooks for school? Buy notebooks made from recycled paper. If even one in every 10 students switched to recycled notebooks this year, an unbelievable 60,000 trees and 25.5 million gallons of water could be saved.

- Grabbing a quick bite to eat? Try something other than a hamburger. Skipping one quarter-pound burger can conserve 600 gallons of water.

- Get your parents to buy a compact fluorescent light bulb for your room. If you replace just one <u>incandescent lamp</u> with a

The *I Buy Different* campaign, a national environmental education and youth action program of the Center for a New American Dream and World Wildlife Fund, offers five quick ways for teens to make a positive environmental impact by spending differently, not just this Earth Day, but every day.

"With a remarkable $175 billion spent by young people in a year, it is obvious that teens can make a huge difference for the environment by simply purchasing environmentally friendly products," says Judy Braus, director of education at World Wildlife Fund.

"Despite the common myth that kids don't care, surveys have <u>resoundingly</u> shown that teens are incredibly willing to do their part to help protect the environment. In fact according to a Cone/Roper survey, nearly nine out of 10 kids say that they would switch brands to those associated with a good cause," adds Diane Wood, executive director of the Center for a New American Dream. ○

---

## Vo•cab•u•lary

**incandescent lamp** (in kun DES unt lamp) an electric lamp that gives off light when heated by an electric current
**resoundingly** (ree ZOUND ing lee) loudly and clearly

fluorescent one, you can prevent over 262 pounds of carbon dioxide from being released into the atmosphere each year, the leading cause of global warming. Not only does it help the Earth, it will help your parents' budget—they will save more than $25 on their electricity bill over the life of each bulb.

- Checking out the latest cell phone? If you decide to buy a new phone, put your old phone to good use by donating it to a <u>charitable</u> organization rather than throwing it away and clogging landfills.

- Save a car trip. Bike, walk, skate, or take public transportation to get places. Americans only make up 5 percent of the world's population, yet we consume 40 percent of the world's gasoline. **❶**

> **❶ Understanding Cause and Effect** How do these five actions help the environment?

## Answering the BIG Question

As you do the following activities, consider the Big Question:
**What is the American Dream?**

**WRITE TO LEARN** What have you already done to help the environment? What else could you do? Make two lists in your Learner's Notebook: one of efforts you have already been doing and one of ideas you could try.

**LITERATURE GROUPS** Discuss these questions in a small group. What does protecting the environment have to do with the American Dream? Are we obligated to protect the environment? Why or why not?

## Vo•cab•u•lary

**charitable** (CHAIR ih tuh bul) generous or giving

# Happiness in the Johnson family

by Colin Johnson

---

**Is the American Dream about the things we own or the people we love?**

---

I smell butter cookies, hot chocolate and the stickiness
  of sleep

As we gallop up the stairs to the family room

My brother jumping up and down beside me

Like a monkey in his tree-green plaid pajamas

The tree is glowing like a pyramid of <u>radium</u>

And the presents, mysterious cubes and ovals wrapped in
  slippery wax wrapping paper

---

## Vo•cab•u•lary

**radium** (RAY dee um) glowing, radioactive element found in some minerals

The color of fluffy foamy whipped cream

I hope to get a new skateboard or a surfboard

Or any kind of board that moves

I imagine tearing through the boxes to discover the treasure within

We stare at our thumbs as we wait as impatiently as dogs about to be fed

For my parents to wake up so we can open presents

But we only hear our dad snoring

As loud as the howl of the wind on a crisp, cold winter night

But then we turn around and see our rumply <u>tousled</u> parents in the pine-scented hallway

"You can open your presents now," they say

With smiles as wide as two slivers of the moon

"*Finally!*" my brother and I shout as we rush towards the pile of mysterious presents

In the boxes I find root-beer-scented surf wax

A black leash to hold me to my surfboard and my surfboard to me

And foamy grip tape to help me from slipping off the board

And as I hear my mom's graceful laughter

As she watches my brother bounce around the living room

With a ribbon tied around his legs and arms as if he were a present

I feel cozy in a blanket of happiness and love ❶

❶ **Determining Main Idea**
What is the main idea, or message of this poem?

---

## Vo·cab·u·lary

**tousled** (TOW zuld) ruffled; untidy

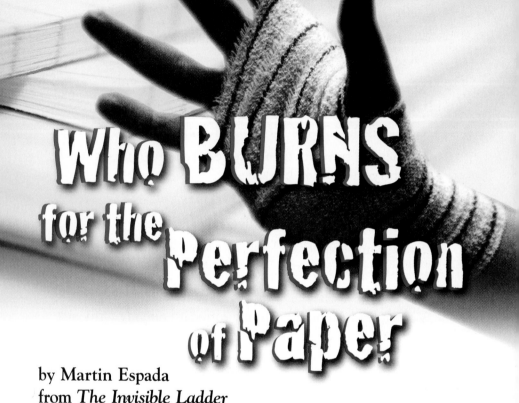

# Who BURNS for the Perfection of Paper

by Martin Espada
from *The Invisible Ladder*

**Who are the people who make our lifestyle possible?**

At sixteen, I worked after high school hours
at a printing plant
that manufactured legal pads:
Yellow paper
stacked seven feet high
and leaning

as I slipped cardboard
between the pages,
then brushed red glue
up and down the stack.
No gloves: fingertips required
for the perfection of paper,
smoothing the exact rectangle.
Sluggish by 9 PM, the hands
would slide along suddenly sharp paper,
and gather slits thinner than the crevices
of the skin, hidden.
Then the glue would sting,
hands oozing
till both palms burned
at the punchclock.
Ten years later, in law school, **2**
I knew that every legal pad
was glued with the sting of hidden cuts,
that every open lawbook
was a pair of hands
upturned and burning.

**2 Analyzing**
How does this poem help you understand and appreciate the dignity of manual labor?

---

## Vo•cab•u•lary

**sluggish** (SLUG ish) slow
**crevices** (KRE vus uz) deep cracks

They Are Planning to Cancel the School Milk Program to Fund a Tax Cut for the Middle Class

by Liz Rosenberg

**Sometimes one person's gain is another person's loss.**

So the milk carton which used to wobble
on the little metal desk will no longer arrive,
and the child will drink instead from the school water
    fountain

and have a little less
each day a little less—
but now there will be more empty space, more room
in her <u>rumpled</u> paper bag!
and more room on the school desk
which is clamped with metal <u>rivets</u> to her chair.
And the middle-class man will wash his car
more often, the middle-class woman wash her hair
at a stylist's, like a decent person,
and the child at the desk with one square
carton missing may find room to think
  thoughts
that will bring the stars, the clouds,
  the trees
around our heads! **3** ○

**3 Author's Perspective**
How does the writer express her feelings about the tax cut through the speaker in the poem?

---

## Answering the BIG Question

As you do the following activities, consider the Big Question:
**What is the American Dream?**

**WRITE TO LEARN** Think about what each poem has to say about the American Dream. Pick one poem and write an entry in your Learner's Notebook about how the poet or main characters experience the American Dream.

**PARTNER TALK** Who are the winners and the losers in the poem by Liz Rosenberg? Do people sometimes achieve the American Dream at the expense of others? Discuss these questions with a classmate.

---

## Vo•cab•u•lary

**rumpled** (RUM puld) wrinkled; puckered
**rivets** (RIV itz) kinds of nails or bolts

# The Hungry Coat

## A Tale from Turkey

### by Demi

**What makes a person worthwhile?**

Once upon a time in Turkey there lived a funny, little wise man named Nasrettin Hoca. He wore a huge, white turban and a worn-out coat made of patches upon patches. Riding about on his little gray donkey, he liked to help whomever he could.

One day Nasrettin Hoca heard a great commotion inside a caravansary, a <u>hostel</u> for travelers. A frisky goat had gotten loose inside the kitchen. Kicking and prancing, she was breaking all the dishes, knocking over pots and pans, and spilling all the cooking oil. The cook was screaming, and a few travelers were slipping in the oil as they tried to catch the goat.

Because he loved goats so much, Nasrettin always carried a sweet apple in his pocket for them. He quickly took out the apple and cut it into little pieces. He lined up the pieces, so as the little goat nibbled to the last piece, Nasrettin was able to catch her.

Gently Nasrettin put the little goat back into her pen, and

## Vo·cab·u·lary

**hostel** (HAWS tul) a kind of inexpensive hotel

everyone cheered. The caravansary owner invited Nasrettin to eat with the other travelers, but Nasrettin declined, as he was on his way to a <u>banquet</u> at the home of a rich friend.

Nasrettin trotted off, waving to all and happy to have helped. He was so late now that he realized he would not have time to change his coat, which was not only worn-out with patches upon patches but also oily, dirty, and smelling of goat.

When Nasrettin's friend opened the door to Nasrettin, he was shocked. He was afraid his other guests would laugh at him for being friends with such a <u>shabby</u>, smelly man.

Nasrettin simply jumped off his donkey, hugged his friend, and joined the banquet. He was so happy to be among friends that for a while he didn't notice something very strange: No one was facing him!

All the guests had turned their backs toward Nasrettin. And when the servants brought dinner into the room, the food was served to everyone but him!

Before long, Nasrettin was left sitting alone with nothing at all to eat. Several times he tried to start a conversation by yelling to a guest at the opposite side of the room, but no one listened and no one responded.

Nasrettin looked thoughtfully at his friends. Each man was scrubbed until he glistened. Each one was wearing his best coat. Then Nasrettin looked down at his own coat—worn-out with patches upon patches, oily, dirty, and smelling of goat.

Very quickly Nasrettin slipped out the door. He mounted his little donkey and began trotting home, when he had an idea.

At home Nasrettin jumped into a tub of hot water, poured in a whole jar of perfumed soap crystals, and scrubbed himself until he glistened and the whole room was filled with bubbles.

Nasrettin dried and powdered himself. Then he put on new

---

## Vo•cab•u•lary

**banquet** (BAYN kwit) a large feast
**shabby** (SHAB ee) well worn; nearly worn out

shoes with <u>tassled</u> toes, a magnificent new turban with sparkling jewels, and a fine new coat of shining silk with golden threads.

Nasrettin <u>preened</u> himself before a mirror. Never had he been so completely well dressed. Never had anyone worn a coat like this one. How fine he looked!

Nasrettin strutted out of his house. Everyone nodded respectfully as he <u>swaggered</u> along the street, heading back to his rich friend's home.

A servant ushered Nasrettin into the banquet hall, and his smiling host immediately served him food and drink. Everyone smiled and nodded at Nasrettin. What a fine figure he made! What a fine coat! Nasrettin was the most popular man at the banquet!

Nasrettin picked up the choicest grilled lamb chop. But instead of putting it in his mouth, Nasrettin put it inside his coat!

"Eat, coat! Eat!" said Nasrettin.

Nasrettin picked up fish fried in vine leaves and roasted eggplant. Opening his coat, he said, "Eat, coat! Eat!"

Nasrettin scooped up pilaf, raisins, and pistachio nuts. Opening his coat, he said, "Eat, coat! Eat!"

Boiled squash stuffed with hash and olives went into the coat. "Eat, coat! Eat!"

Slices of chicken breast stewed in rose water, sugar cakes, flavored jellies, sherbet, sticky baklava, pomegranates, persimmons, oranges, apples, figs, and dates—all of this food Nasrettin stuffed into his bulging coat, shouting, "Eat, coat! Eat!"

Finally Nasrettin opened his coat once more and poured a whole bottle of wine inside. Then, closing his coat as best as he could, Nasrettin patted his belly and smiled at his host.

---

## Vo•cab•u•lary

**tassled** (TAS uld) having tassles, decorative pieces of string or ribbon tied onto the end of something
**preened** (preend) admired oneself
**swaggered** (SWAG urd) strutted; walked proudly

All the guests were amazed! What was Nasrettin doing?

At last, the alarmed host said, "Tell me, my old friend, why are you feeding your coat?"

"Surely you wanted my coat to eat," Nasrettin replied. "When I first arrived in my old coat made of patches upon patches, there was no food for me. Yet when I came back in this new coat, there was every kind of food for me. This shows it was the coat—and not me—that you invited to your banquet!"

"Remember this, my friends," said Nasrettin Hoca. "If you want to look deeply, look at the man and not at his coat. You can change the coat, but you cannot change the man. A coat may be fine, but a coat does not make a man. Outside a man may wear a sheepskin, but inside he may wear the heart of a wolf! Many a good man may be found under a shabby coat. With coats, new are the best. But with friends, old are the best!"

Everyone cheered.

"The wisdom of Nasrettin Hoca calls for celebration!" exclaimed the host. Music and fireworks resounded, and everyone danced under the stars of heaven. ❶ ○

**❶ Determining Main Ideas**
What is the main idea, or message, of this story?

---

## Answering the BIG Question

As you do the following activities, consider the Big Question:
**What is the American Dream?**

**WRITE TO LEARN** People are often judged by their clothing and apearance, as in this story. Think of a time when you made a mistaken judgment about a person based on his or her apearance. Describe the experience in your Learner's Notebook.

**PARTNER TALK** For many people, the American Dream includes having lots of material things. What would Nasrettin Hoca say about those who value posessions so highly? Discuss this issue with a partner who has read this story.

# Index of Authors and Titles

# Index of Authors and Titles

# Acknowledgments

## Literature credits

### Unit 5

"Open Mike: Zorro by Raul Ramirez," "Diondra Jordan," "Devon Hope," "Open Mike: Bronx Masquerade by Devon Hope," "Tyrone," from *Bronx Masquerade* by Nikki Grimes, copyright © 2002 by Nikki Grimes. Used by permission of Dial Books for Young Readers, A Division of Penguin Young Readers Group, A Member of Penguin Group (USA) inc., 345 Hudson Street, New York, NY 10014. All rights reserved.

"5 Clever Survivors" by Aline Alexander Newman, *National Geographic Kids,* November 2004. Copyright © 2004 National Geographic Society. Reprinted by permission.

"Rough Touch" by Lucy Bledsoe. Reprinted by permission of the author.

"Coach's Son" from *Poems from Homeroom* by Kathi Appelt. Copyright © 2002 by Kathi Appelt. Reprinted by permission of Henry Holt and Company, LLC.

"Poem for my Sister" from *Dreaming Frankenstein* by Liz Lochhead is reproduced by permission of Polygon, an imprint of Berlinn Ltd.

"My Look Says Nothing About Who I Am" by Michael Logan, from *What Are You? Voices of Mixed-Race Young People,* edited by Pearl Fuyo Gaskins. Published by Henry Holt and Co., 1999. Copyright © 1999 by Pearl Fuyo Gaskins.

"Why Are People Staring at Me?" by Nicole Rivera, from *What Are You? Voices of Mixed-Race Young People,* edited by Pearl Fuyo Gaskins. Published by Henry Holt and Co., 1999. Copyright © 1999 by Pearl Fuyo Gaskins.

"Being Indian" by Dana Mathias, from *When the Rain Sings,* National Mueum of the American Indian, Smithsonian Institution in association with Simon & Schuster Books for Young Readers. Copyright © by Dana Mathias.

"Thoughts of the Different" by Adi Givati, from *The Pain Tree and Other Teenage Angst-Ridden Poetry,* collected by Esther Pearl Watson and Mark Todd. Copyright © 2000 by Adi Givati. Reprinted by permission of Houghton Mifflin Company. All rights reserved.

"9 Drawbacks to Being Popular" from *The Book of Lists for Teens* by Sandra and Harry Choron. Copyright © 2002 by Sandra Choron. Reprinted by permission of Houghton Mifflin Company. All rights reserved.

"Keep Staring: I Might Do a Trick" by Willem Winkelman, as told to Rachel Buchholz. *National Geographic Kids,* November 2004. Copyright © 2004 National Geographic Society. Reprinted by permission.

"Follow the Water" by Jennifer L. Holm from *Shelf Life: Stories by the Book,* edited by Gary Paulsen. Copyright © 2003 by Jennifer L. Holm. Reprinted by permission of Simon & Schuster Books for Young Readers.

### Unit 6

"What's the Worst That Could Happen?" by Bruce Coville. Reprinted by permission of the author.

"Spring 1954: Richmond, Virginia" from *Defending the Spirit: A Black Life in America* by Randall Robinson, copyright © 1998 by Randall Robinson. Used by permission of Dutton, a division of Penguin Group (USA) Inc.

"Blinking" by Morton Marcus. Reprinted by permission of the author.

"David" by William I. Elliott. Reprinted by permission of the author.

"Incident" by Countee Cullen. Copyrights held by Amistad Research Center, Tulane University, administered by Thompson and Thompson, Brooklyn, NY.

"Balance" by June A. English, from *Girls Got Game: Sports Stories and Poems,* edited by Sue Macy. Published by Henry Holt and Co., 2001. Compilation copyright © 2001 by Sue Macy.

# Acknowledgments

*From* "Maximum Pressure: Teens Face Stress Every Day. Here's How to Calm Down Your Life" by Nancy Fitzgerald. Published in *Scholastic Choices*, September 2004. Copyright © 2004 by Scholastic Inc. Reprinted by permission.

"Kemba's Story" from www.abouthealth.com/t_topicX.htm?topic=41

"Thief of the Nile" by Craig Sodaro, from *Plays, the Drama Magazine for Young People*, reprinted with the permission of the publisher Plays/Sterling Partners, Inc. Copyright © 2005. Plays, PO Box 600160, Newton, MA 02460.

## Unit 7

"Jackie Robinson, Baseball's Pathfinder" by Ruth Dorfman. Reprinted by permission of the author.

"For my 'pen pal' in Louisiana: Video asks about life after Katrina" by Kerry Murakami, *Seattle Post-Intelligencer*, November 21, 2005. Reprinted by permission of the Seattle Post-Intelligencer.

"The Dive" from *Finding our Way* by René Saldaña, Jr., copyright © 2003 by René Saldaña, Jr. Used by permission of Random House Children's Books, a division of Random House, Inc.

"Sleepless at Sea" by Naila Moreira, from *Science News for Kids*, July 13, 2005. Reprinted with permission from *Science News for Kids*, copyright © 2005.

"Sleeping Soundly for a Longer Life" by Emily Sohn, from *Science News for Kids*, February 12, 2003. Reprinted with permission from *Science News for Kids*, copyright © 2003.

"Casey at the Bat" by Ernest Lawrence Thayer.

Excerpt from *A Single Shard* by Linda Sue Park. Copyright © 2001 by Linda Sue Park. Reprinted by permission of Clarion Books, an imprint of Houghton Mifflin Company. All rights reserved.

"It's Just a Question" from *Jazmin's Notebook* by Nikki Grimes, copyright © 1998 by Nikki Grimes. Used by permission of Dial Books for Young Readers, A Division of Penguin Young Readers Group, A Member of Penguin Group (USA) inc., 345 Hudson Street, New York, NY 10014. All rights reserved.

Excerpt from *Strive Toward Freedom* reprinted by arrangement with the Estate of Martin Luther King Jr., c/o Writer's House as agent for the proprietor, New York, NY. Copyright © 1958 by Martin Luther King Jr., copyright renewed 1986 by Coretta Scott King.

"Phoenix Farm" by Jane Yolen. Copyright © 1996 by Jane Yolen. Originally appeared in *Bruce Coville's Book of Magic* (Apple/Scholastic), edited by Bruce Coville. Now appears in *Twelve Impossible Things Before Breakfast* by Jane Yolen, published by Harcourt Brace 1997. Reprinted by permission of Curtis Brown Ltd.

"Ida Battles Big Oil," by Ruth Spencer Johnson, from COBBLESTONE's March 2005 issue: *Muckrakers*, copyright © 2005, Carus Publishing Company, published by Cobblestone Publishing, 30 Grove Street, Suite C, Peterborough, NH 03458. All rights reserved. Used by permission of the publisher.

## Unit 8

"The Screamin' Eagles Help Students Soar" from *Heroes and Helpers*, copyright © 2003 World Book, Inc. By permission of the publisher. www.worldbook.com.

Excerpt from "Forced Out" from *Breaking Through* by Francisco Jimenez. Copyright © 2001 by Francisco Jimenez. Reprinted by permission of Houghton Mifflin Company. All rights reserved.

"The American Dream: Happiness, Say Teens" by Mirandi Hitti, from WebMD Medical News. Copyright © 2004 WebMD, Inc.

"Barack Obama's Keynote Speech" by Barack Obama, from www.usconstitution.net/obama (Based on a transcript presented by the *New York Times*)

*from* "Building Bridges" by Andrea Davis Pinkney. Published in *Stay True: Short Stories for Strong Girls* compiled by Marilyn Singer. Published by Scholastic Press/Scholastic Inc. Copyright © 1998 Andrea Davis Pinkney. Reprinted by permission.

"In Step With: Wilmer Valderrama" *Parade*, January 1, 2006. Copyright © 2006 Parade Magazine. All rights reserved. Reprinted with permission.

"5 Ways Teens Can Spend Smarter for a Cleaner, Greener Earth." Reprinted by permission of The Center for a New American Dream, www.newdream.org.

"Happiness in the Johnson Family" by Colin Johnson, age 11. Reprinted with permission from *Stone Soup, the magazine by young writers and artists.* Copyright © 2005 by the Children's Art Foundation.

"Who Burns for the Perfection of Paper" from *City of Coughing and Dead Radiators* by Martin Espada. Copyright © 1993 by Martin Espada. Used by permission of W. W. Norton & Company, Inc.

"They Are Planning to Cancel the School Milk Program to Fund a Tax Cut for the Middle Class" from *The Invisible Ladder* by Liz Rosenberg. Copyright © 1996 by Liz Rosenberg. Reprinted by permission of Henry Holt and Company, LLC.

Reprinted with the permission of Margaret K. McElderry Books, an imprint of Simon & Schuster's Children's Publishing Division, from *The Hungry Coat* by Demi. Copyright © 2004 by Demi.

Glencoe would like to acknowledge the artists who participated in illustrating this program: Cathryn Hahn, Ben Shannon, Jan Klinkbeil, Kagan McLeod, and Donovan Foote.

## Photo credits

**Cover i** (tr bkgd flame)Don Farral/Getty Images, (tr inset hawk)Geostock/Getty Images, (cl inset swimmer)Index Open, (cl bkgd galaxy)Terry Why/Index Open, (bl)Mel Curtis/Getty Images, (br)R.Strange/Getty Images; **iv v** Cut and Deal Ltd./Index Open; **0** (inset)Mel Curtis/Getty Images, (bkgd)2006 JupiterImages Corporation/photos. com, (bkgd)CORBIS/2006 JupiterImages Corporation, (bkgd)Tomi/Getty Images; **1** (l)RubberBall, (r)RubberBall (inset)Darryl Lenuik/Getty Images; **2** F. Schussler/Getty Images; **3** CORBIS; **5** Ryan McVay/Getty Images; **7** AbleStock/Index Open; **8** James Gritz/Getty Images; **10** Getty Images; **12** Ryan McVay/Getty Images; **13** Chip Simons/Getty Images; **15** (inset)Vicky Kasala/Getty Images, (bkgd)AbleStock/Index Open; **19** Steve Cole/Getty Images; **20** Getty Images/ SW Productions; **22** 2006 JupiterImages Corporation/photos.com; **23** Camille Tokerud/ Getty Images; **24 37** 2006 JupiterImages Corporation/photos.com; **38** Image100 Ltd.; **39** DesignPics/IndexOpen; **42** Scott T. Baxter/Getty Images; **43** 2006 JupiterImages Corporation/photos.com; **44** Vstock; **46** Image Source/2006 JupiterImages Corporation; **47** 2006 JupiterImages Corporation/photos. com; **49** Acey Harper/Time Life Pictures/Getty Images; **50** (inset)IndexOpen, (bkgd)Terry Why/IndexOpen; **53** StockTrek/Getty Images; **57** Brand X Pictures/Punchstock; **60** photo library.com/Index Open; **62** photos.com/Index Open; **65** Brand X Pictures/Punchstock; **68** photos.com/Index Open; **70** Digital Vision/ Punchstock; **74** (inset)David Ridley/Getty Images, (bkgd)Comstock; **76** PictureQuest; **78** photolibrary.com/IndexOpen; **81** Jack Hollingsworth/Getty Images; **83**Comstock/ Alamy; **84** Comstock; **87** Shipes Shooter/ Stockfood America; **90** (l)Getty Images, (r)CORBIS; **105** Getty Images; **106** (t)Getty Images, (bl)Getty Images, (br)C Squared Studios/Getty Images; **107** Stockbyte; **108** Vstock/Index Open; **110** C Squared Studios/Getty Images; **111 115** Getty Images; **117** DesignPics/IndexOpen; **119** Image100 Ltd.; **120** Vstock/IndexOpen; **124** Big Cheese Photo/PictureQuest; **126** Dave & Les Jacobs/Getty Images; **128** R.Strange/Getty Images; **130** Vstock/IndexOpen; **132** J.C. Kanny/Lorpresse/CORBIS; **134** AbleStock/ IndexOpen; **136** Sandro Vannini/CORBIS; **139** CORBIS; **141** Dynamic Graphics/2006 JupiterImages Corporation; **143** 2006 JupiterImages Corporation/photos.com; **145** R.Strange/Getty Images; **148** Bob Sandberg/Look Magazine Photograph Collection; **150 151 152** RubberBall; **153** AP/ Wide World Photos; **154** Chad Baker/Ryan McVay/Getty Images; **156** Burke/Triolo/Brand X Pictures/2006 JupiterImages Corporation; **157** Steve Cole/Getty Images; **158** RubberBall/Getty Images; **163** Jonnie Miles/ Getty Images; **167** SeaWorld San Diego/Mike Aguilera/AP/Wide World Photos; **170 172** Getty Images; **176** Rim Light/Getty Images; **178** Digital Vision/PunchStock; **181** CORBIS; **183** Image100 Ltd.; **197** (l)AP/Wide World Photos, (r)Pan American Airways/AP/Wide World Photos; **200** (t)Don Farral/Getty Images, (b)Geostock/Getty Images; **203** Getty Images; **204** Siede Preis/Getty Images; **205** (l)Don Farral/Getty Images, (r)Geostock/ Getty Images; **206** Tom Stewart/CORBIS; **207** (tl inset Tarbell)The Ida M.Tarbell Collection, Pelletier Library, Allegheny College, (bkgd)Texas Energy Museum, (tl bkgd frame) Beaumont, Texas, 1996 Image Farm; **208 209** Texas Energy Museum, Beaumont, Texas; **211** Getty Images; **212** (inset)AP/Wide World Photos, (bkgd)Image Source/Getty Images; **214** RubberBall/Getty Images; **215** Ryan McVay/Getty Images; **217** Susan Sterner/AP/Wide World Photos; **218** Lenny Ignelzi/AP/Wide World Photos; **220** Doug Kanter/AP/Wide World Photos; **222** Damian Dovarganes/AP/Wide World Photos; **224** (t)Stockbyte/Getty Images, (tc)Andy

# Acknowledgments

Sortiriou/Getty Images, (b)Index Stock
Photography/Getty Images, (bc)Christopher
Kerrigan/The McGraw-Hill Companies;
**226** Getty Images; **227** Ron Edmonds/
AP/Wide World Photos; **228** CORBIS;
**230** Seth Perlman/AP/Wide World Photos;
**232** (inset)SW Productions/Getty Images,
(bkgd)Getty Images; **237** C Squared Studios/
Getty Images; **239** (inset)Rudi Von Briel/
Index Open, (bkgd)Burke/Triolo/Brand X
Pictures/2006 JupiterImages Corporation;
**242** Getty Images; **245** C Squared
Studios/Getty Images; **246** Getty Images;
**248 250** Knight-Ridder/Tribune Media
Information Services; **263** (tl)Stockbyte/
PictureQuest, (tr)2006 JupiterImages
Corporation/photos.com, (tc)2006
JupiterImages Corporation/photos.com,
(c)John A. Rizzo/Getty Images, (cr)Comstock/
Alamy, (bc)C Squared Studios/Getty Images,
(bkgd)2006 JupiterImages Corporation/photos.
com; **264** StockTreck/Getty Images; **266** Art
Vandalay/Getty Images; **268** (inset)Laurent
Hamels/PictureQuest, (bkgd)2006
JupiterImages Corporation/photos.com; **270**
Jonnie Miles/Getty Images; **272** (t)Kevin
Sanchez/Cole Group/Getty Images, (cl)
PhotoAlto/PunchStock, (cr)S. Pearce/Getty
Images, (tr)none, (bl)Getty Images, (br)John
A. Rizzo/Getty Images.